a BOOK Of CHORALES

and supplemental hymns

Compiled by

FREDERICK R. DARIES, D.D.
Indianapolis, Indiana

Published by

EDEN PUBLISHING HOUSE
Saint Louis, Missouri

Preface

The compiler of this Book of Chorales and Supplemental Hymns comes from a church body, in which, for many years, only chorales were sung in the services of worship. When later other hymn books appeared, the congregations learned to appreciate the many other types of hymns. It is evident that all chorales, that had been used, could not be included in the newer hymn books. Several denominations, whose members were not well acquainted with chorales, did, however, include many of the better known ones in their hymnals. We do not expect this book to replace any hymnal now in use. It will, however, be suitable for choirs and choral groups, for many of these are already using chorales as anthems in the services of worship and for special occasions. Some melodies included among the chorales can be considered carols or hymns. But they have been long associated with chorales and are thus accepted quite generally by the church. In publishing this book, a dream of many years is being realized, namely, to have the chorales, even some that are not so well known, published in a single book. The congregation in Indianapolis, Indiana, of which the undersigned has been a minister for over thirty-eight years, is nobly supporting this effort.

In compiling these chorales and hymns our main concern has been to preserve the melodies, which have become dear to so many. Most of the translations convey the thoughts that were expressed and used with the melodies for many years. Since it was not possible to find any translation for some of the chorales, words of the correct meter were used. Of necessity, many lovely melodies had to be omitted. The chorales used have, after counselling with interested persons, been considered the best known ones.

In the Supplemental Hymns there are melodies, which have been taken from Church School hymnals of years ago. Many are of the semi-chorale nature and should also be preserved. Some have already been incorporated in our modern hymnals.

We pray that this book may be a source of great blessing to all who use it. "So will I sing praise to Thy name forever." Psalm 61: 8.

Frederick R. Daries

1 Now Thank We All Our God

NUN DANKET ALLE GOTT

Martin Rinkart, 1586-1649
Tr. Catherine Winkworth, 1858   **6. 7. 6. 7. 6. 6. 6. 6.**   Johann Crüger, 1648

Majestically, but not too slowly

1. Now thank we all our God With heart, and hands, and voi - ces,
2. O may this boun-teous God Through all our life be near us,
3. All praise and thanks to God, The Fa-ther, now be giv - en,

Who won-drous things hath done, In whom His world re - joi - ces;
With ev - er joy - ful hearts And bless-ed peace to cheer us;
The Son, and Him who reigns With them in high - est heav - en,

Who from our moth - ers' arms Hath blest us on our way
To keep us in His grace, And guide us when per - plexed,
The One E - ter - nal God, Whom earth and heaven a - dore;

With count - less gifts of love, And still is ours to - day.
And free us from all ills In this world and the next.
For thus it was, is now, And shall be ev - er - more. A-MEN.

(1)

2   Jehovah, Let Me Now Adore Thee

Bartholomäus Crasselius, 1697
Tr. Catherine Winkworth, 1858

9. 10. 9. 10. 10. 10.

DIR, DIR, JEHOVAH
Geistreiches *Gesangbuch*
Halle, 1704

With exaltation

1. Je - ho - vah, let me now a - dore Thee, For where is there a
2. O Fa - ther, draw me to my Sav - iour That Thy dear Son may
3. Grant that Thy Spir - it prompt my prais - es, Then shall my sing - ing
4. For He can plead for me with sigh - ings That are un - speak - a -

Lord, O God, as Thou? With songs I fain would come be - fore Thee;
draw me un - to Thee; Thy Spir - it guide my whole be - hav - ior
sure - ly please Thine ear; Sweet are the sounds my heart then rais - es,
ble to lips like mine; He bids me pray with ear - nest cry - ings,

Oh, let Thy Ho - ly Spir - it teach me now To praise Thee in His
And rule both sense and rea - son thus in me That, Lord, Thy peace from
My prayer in truth and spir - it Thou wilt hear. Then shall Thy Spir - it
Bears wit - ness with my soul that I am Thine, Joint heir with Christ, and

name thro' whom a - lone Our songs can please Thee, thro' Thy bless - ed Son!
me may ne'er de - part, But wake sweet mel - o - dies with - in my heart.
raise my heart to Thee To sing Thee psalms of praise in high de - gree.
thus may dare to say: O heav'n - ly Fa - ther, hear me when I pray! A-MEN.

3

All Glory Be to God on High

ALLEIN GOTT IN DER HÖH' SEI EHR'

Nicolaus Decius, 1526
Tr. Catherine Winkworth, 1862, alt.   8. 7. 8. 7. 8. 8. 7.

Adapted from plain song
Deutsch Evangelisch Messze, 1539

Joyously, but with dignity

1. All glo-ry be to God on high, Who hath our race be-friend-ed!
2. We praise, we wor-ship Thee, we trust And give Thee thanks for-ev - er,
3. O Je - sus Christ, our God and Lord, Be - got-ten of the Fa - ther,
4. O Ho - ly Spir-it, pre-cious Gift, Thou Com-fort-er un-fail - ing,

To us no harm shall now come nigh, The strife at last is end - ed;
O Fa-ther, that Thy rule is just And wise, and chan-ges nev - er;
O Thou who hast our peace re-stored, And the lost sheep dost gath - er,
Do Thou our trou-bled souls up-lift, A - gainst the foe pre-vail - ing;

God show-eth His good-will to men, And peace shall reign on
Thy bound-less power o'er all things reigns, Thou dost what-e'er Thy
Thou Lamb of God, en-throned on high, Be - hold our need and
A - vert our woes and calm our dread: For us the Sav-iour's

earth a - gain; O thank Him for His good - ness!
will or - dains; 'Tis well Thou art our Rul - er!
hear our cry; Have mer - cy on us, Je - sus!
blood was shed; Do Thou in faith sus - tain us! A - MEN.

4 Praise Ye the Lord, the Almighty

Joachim Neander, 1680
Tr. Catherine Winkworth, 1863

14. 14. 4. 7. 8.

LOBE DEN HERREN
Stralsund Gesangbuch, 1665
Arr. in *Praxis Pietatis Melica,* 1668

1. Praise ye the Lord, the Al-might-y, the King of cre-a - tion!
2. Praise ye the Lord, who o'er all things so won-drous-ly reign - eth,
3. Praise ye the Lord, O let all that is in me a - dore Him!

O my soul, praise Him, for He is thy health and sal-va - tion!
Shel-ters thee un-der His wings, yea, so gent-ly sus-tain - eth!
All that hath life and breath, come now with prais-es be - fore Him!

All ye who hear, Now to His tem - ple draw near;
Hast thou not seen How thy de - sires e'er have been
Let the A - men Sound from His peo - ple a - gain:

Join me in glad ad - o - ra - - - tion!
Grant - ed in what He or - dain - - - eth?
Glad - ly for aye we a - dore Him. A - MEN.

5   O That I Had a Thousand Voices

FRANKFURT

Johann Mentzer, 1658-1743, tr.   9. 8. 9. 8. 8. 8.   J. Balth. König's *Liederschatz*, 1738

Majestically

1. O that I had a thou-sand voi - ces, A mouth to speak with thou-sand tongues! Then, with a heart His praise re - joi - ces, Would I pro-claim in grate-ful songs To all wher-ev-er I should be, What 'tis the Lord has done for me.

2. O that my voice might high be sound - ing, Far as the wide-ly dis - tant poles; My blood be quick with rap - ture bound - ing, Long as its vi - tal cur-rent rolls: And ev - 'ry pulse thanks-giv - ing raise, And ev - 'ry breath a hymn of praise!

3. Dear Fa - ther, end - less praise I ren - der, For soul and bod - y strange-ly joined: I praise Thee, Guard-ian kind and ten - der, For all the no - ble joys I find So rich - ly spread on ev - 'ry side, And free - ly for my use sup - plied.

4. For all Thy good - ness I'll ex - tol Thee, While yet my tongue has strength to move; First ob - ject of my love en - roll Thee, Un - til my heart for - get to love. When fee - ble lips no voice can raise, My dy - ing sighs shall mur - mur praise. A - MEN.

6 Praise Thou the Lord, O My Soul, Now Praise Him

J. Daniel Herrnschmidt, 1675-1723
Tr. C. G. Haas, 1897, alt.

LOBE DEN HERREN, O MEINE SEELE (Halle)
Freylinghausen's *Geistreiches Gesangbuch*, 1704
10. 8. 10. 8. 8. 8. 4. 4.

With exaltation

1. Praise thou the Lord, O my soul, now praise Him, His praise con-
tin - ue un - til death; While I the path - ways of
earth am tread - ing God shall be praised with ev - ery breath.
My soul and bod - y He did give, And waits my praise from

2. Hap - py, yea, hap - py are they for - ev - er Whose help the
God of Ja - cob is, Who hath cre - at - ed the
earth and heav - en, The sea and all that there - in is.
Let all the world His prais - es sing, Who life and health to

3. If there are an - y who are op - press - ed, He work - eth
jus - tice in the tide; Food for the hun - gry, for-
lorn, dis - tress - ed, The Lord in sea - son doth pro - vide;
Those bound in chains He mak - eth free, His lov - ing - kind - ness

4. Praise, O ye peo - ple, the Name most glo - rious Of Him who
reigns Al - might - y King: Let all u - nite in one
ho - ly cho - rus To God our hymns of joy to bring.
O Zi - on, with the heaven - ly host, Praise Fa - ther, Son, and

Praise Thou the Lord, O My Soul, Now Praise Him

morn till eve, O praise the Lord, O praise the Lord!
all doth bring, O praise the Lord, O praise the Lord!
they shall see, O praise the Lord, O praise the Lord!
Ho - ly Ghost, O praise the Lord, O praise the Lord! A - MEN.

Words copyright, 1941, Eden Publishing House.

BEGINNING of WORSHIP

7 ## Open Now Thy Gates of Beauty

Benjamin Schmolck, 1732
Tr. Catherine Winkworth, 1863, alt.   8. 7. 8. 7. 7. 7.

UNSER HERRSCHER (Neander)
Joachim Neander, 1680

In moderate time and graceful rhythm

1. O - pen now thy gates of beau-ty, Zi - on, let me en - ter there,
2. Gra - cious God I come be - fore Thee, Come Thou al - so down to me;
3. Speak, O Lord, and I will hear Thee, Let Thy will be done in - deed;

Where my soul in joy - ful du - ty Waits for Him who an - swers prayer:
Where we find Thee and a - dore Thee, There a heaven on earth must be:
May I un - dis-turbed draw near Thee While Thou dost Thy peo - ple feed.

O how bless - ed is this place, Filled with sol - ace, light, and grace!
To my heart O en - ter Thou, Let it be Thy tem - ple now.
Here of life the foun-tain flows, Here is balm for all our woes. A-MEN.

(7)

8 Sing Praise to God Who Reigns Above

Johann Jacob Schuetz, 1673
Tr. Frances Elizabeth Cox, 1864

8. 7. 8. 7. 8. 8. 7.

WITTENBERG
Joh. Walther's *Gesangbuch*, 1524

With confidence and joy

1. Sing praise to God who reigns a - bove, The God of all cre - a - - tion, The God of pow'r, the God of love, The God of our sal - va - - tion; With heal - ing balm my soul He fills, And ev - 'ry faith - less mur - mur stills; To God all praise and glo - ry!

2. The an - gel host, O King of kings, Thy praise for - ev - er tell - - ing, In earth and sky all liv - ing things, Be - neath Thy shad - ow dwell - ing, A - dore the wis - dom which could span, And pow'r which formed cre - a - tion's plan; To God all praise and glo - ry!

3. I cried to God in my dis - tress, His mer - cy heard me call - - ing; My Sav - iour saw my help - less - ness, And kept my feet from fall - - ing; For this, Lord, praise and thanks to Thee! Praise God Most High, praise God with me! To God all praise and glo - ry!

4. Thus all my glad - some way a - long I'll sing a - loud Thy prais - es, That men may hear the grate - ful song My voice un - wea - ried rais - - es: Be joy - ful in the Lord, my heart! Both soul and bod - y, bear your part! To God all praise and glo - ry! A-MEN.

9 God of Might, We Praise Thy Name

GROSSER GOTT WIR LOBEN DICH
Katholisches Gesangbuch, Vienna, c. 1774

Ignaz Franz, 1771
Tr. J. H. Horstmann, 1908

7. 8. 7. 8. 7. 7.

Not too slowly

1. God of might, we praise Thy name For Thy deeds of
2. Cher - u - bim and ser - a - phim Praise Thy name with
3. All Thy Church in ev - ery land Lifts it voice in
4. Look up - on Thy chil - dren here Who, their love for

strength and glo - ry, Heaven and earth ex - tol Thy fame,
joy un - ceas - ing; Proph - ets and a - pos - tles are
ad - o - ra - tion Un - to Thee, O God of Love,
Thee pro - fess - ing, And in Je - sus' name a - lone,

And pro - claim the bless - ed sto - ry: As Thou art, Thou
Ev - er - more Thy praise in - creas - ing, And the mar - tyrs,
For Thy work of man's sal - va - tion; Thou art King of
Ask of Thee a Fa - ther's bless - ing;] When the course of

e'er wilt be Un - to all e - ter - ni - ty.
brave and true, Wor - ship Thee with prais - es new.
Life and Love In Thy heaven - ly realms a - bove.
life is o'er, Bring us home for ev - er - more. A - MEN.

10 Sing My Soul, to God, Who Made Thee

SOLLT ICH MEINEM GOTT NICHT SINGEN
(Cantate Domino)

Paul Gerhardt, 1606-1676
Tr. O. E. Wieland, 1898, alt. 8. 7. 8. 7. 8. 7. 7. 8. 7. 7. Johann Schop, 1641

With confidence and joy

1. Sing, my soul, to God, who made thee, Raise to heaven thy grate-ful voice,
2. E'en the Son He loved so dear-ly Died that we through Him might live,
3. When I sleep His care sur-rounds me, With new strength and youth im-bues;

All His crea-tures, sing-ing, bid thee In His good-ness now re-joice.
Was e'er love like His, who mere-ly Lived His life in love to give?
His un-bound-ed grace con-founds me, Each new morn His love re-news.

Pure and ho-ly love un-bound-ed Fills His ten-der heart and kind;
Ho-ly Spir-it, teach and guide me, Fill my heart with lov-ing faith;
In sore tri-al and temp-ta-tion He, my Sav-iour, still is near,

All who tru-ly serve Him find Rest, by God's strong arm sur-round-ed;
Faith can break the power of death, Naught I fear with Thee be-side me;
Bids me,"Child, do thou not fear, Thou shalt yet see my sal-va-tion."

Heaven and earth may not en-dure, But God's love is ev-er sure. A-MEN.

(10)

11 I Will Ever Sing Thy Praises

WOMIT SOLL ICH DICH WOHL LOBEN
(Gotha)

L. A. Gotter, 1697
Tr. R. A. John, 1912

8. 7. 8. 7. 8. 8. 7. 7.

J. H. Knecht, 1797

1. I will ev-er sing Thy prais-es, Might-y God and gra-cious King;
2. All the peo-ple shall pro-claim Thee, Sing Thy praise from shore to shore;
3. When at last my feet have found Thee, When at last I am Thine own;

Glad my heart its trib-ute rais-es, And to Thee my psalms I sing;
Ev-ery hu-man heart shall name Thee, God and King for-ev-er-more;
When the ran-somed hosts sur-round Thee, On Thy great e-ter-nal throne;

Thou art King of all cre-a-tion, Ev-ery land and ev-ery na-tion;
On Thy throne in heav-en vault-ed, In Thy maj-es-ty ex-alt-ed,
When in yon-der land of glo-ry An-gels tell re-demp-tion's sto-ry,

"Thou-sand, thou-sand thanks to Thee, Might-y God," my song shall be!
"Thou-sand, thou-sand thanks to Thee, Might-y God," my song shall be!
"Thou-sand, thou-sand thanks to Thee, Might-y God," my song shall be! A-MEN.

12

Jehovah, Jehovah

G. K. Pfeffel, 1776
Tr. C. G. Haas, 1897

Irregular

JEHOVAH
Joh. Carl Gerold, 1800

With dignity

Je - ho - vah, Je - ho - vah, Je - ho - vah, Thou art wor - thy

Of hon - or and glo - ry and praise! A - men, A - men! Un -

til the tem - ple of this world By Thy power to dust is hurled,

Help us when these halls we throng, The Ho - ly, Ho - ly, Ho - ly

to pro - long, Hal - le - lu - jah! Hal - le - lu - jah!

(12)

13 Blessed Jesus, at Thy Word

Tobias Clausnitzer, 1663
Tr. Catherine Winkworth, 1858

LIEBSTER JESU WIR SIND HIER (Nüremberg)
7. 8. 7. 8. 8. 8.
Johann Rudolph Ahle, 1664

In moderate time

1. Bless - ed Je - sus, at Thy word We are gath - ered
2. All our knowl - edge, sense, and sight Lie in deep - est
3. Glo - rious Lord, Thy - self im - part! Light of Light, from

all to hear Thee; Let our hearts and souls be stirred
dark - ness shroud - ed, Till Thy Spir - it breaks our night
God pro - ceed - ing, O - pen Thou our ears and heart,

Now to seek and love and fear Thee, By Thy teach - ings
With the beams of truth un - cloud - ed; Thou a - lone to
Help us by Thy Spir - it's plead - ing; Hear the cry Thy

sweet and ho - ly, Drawn from earth to love Thee sole - ly.
God canst win us, Thou must work all good with - in us.
peo - ple rais - es, Hear, and bless our prayers and prais - es. A-MEN.

(13)

14

God Himself Is with Us

WUNDERBARER KÖNIG
Joachim Neander's *Bundes-Lieder*, 1680

Gerhard Tersteegen, 1729
Tr. Composite

6. 6. 8. 6. 6. 8. 3. 3. 6. 6.

1. God Him-self is with us; Let us now a-dore Him,
And with awe ap-pear be-fore Him. God is in His
tem-ple, All with-in keep si-lence, And be-fore Him
bow with rev-erence. Him a-lone, God we own; To our Lord and

2. God Him-self is with us: Whom an-gel-ic le-gions
Serve with awe in heaven-ly re-gions. "Ho-ly, Ho-ly,
Ho-ly," Sing the hosts of heav-en, Praise to God be
ev-er giv-en. Bow Thine ear To us here: Hear, O Christ, the

3. Lord, come dwell with-in us, While on earth we tar-ry,
Make us Thy blest sanc-tu-a-ry, Grant us now Thy
pres-ence, Un-to us draw near-er, And re-veal Thy-
self still clear-er. Where we are, Near or far, Let us see Thy

God Himself Is with Us

Sav - iour Prais - es sing for - ev - er.
prais - es That Thy church now rais - es.
pow - er, Ev - ery day and hour........ A - MEN.

15   Lord Jesus Christ, Be with Us Now

HERR JESU CHRIST, DICH ZU UNS WEND
(Cantionale)

Wilhelm August, II., Duke of Saxe-Weimar, 1638
Tr. Catherine Winkworth, 1862. alt.   L. M.   Pensum Sacrum, 1648

Reverently

1. Lord Je - sus Christ, be with us now, And
2. O teach our lips to sing Thy praise, Our
3. So shall we join the hosts that cry, Ho -
4. Glo - ry to God, the Fa - ther, Son, And

let Thy Ho - ly Spir - it bow All hearts in love and
hearts in true de - vo - tion raise, Strength-en our faith, in -
ly art Thou, O Lord most High! And in the light of
Ho - ly Spir - it, Three in One! To Thee, O bless - ed

fear to - day, To hear the truth, and keep Thy way.
crease our light, That we may do Thy will a - right.
that blest place Shall gaze up - on Thee face to face.
Trin - i - ty, Be praise through-out e - ter - ni - ty. A - MEN.

16   Lord, Dismiss Us with Thy Blessing

John Fawcett, 1773   8. 7. 8. 7.   STUTTGART
Arr. from *Psalmodia Sacra*, 1725

In moderate time

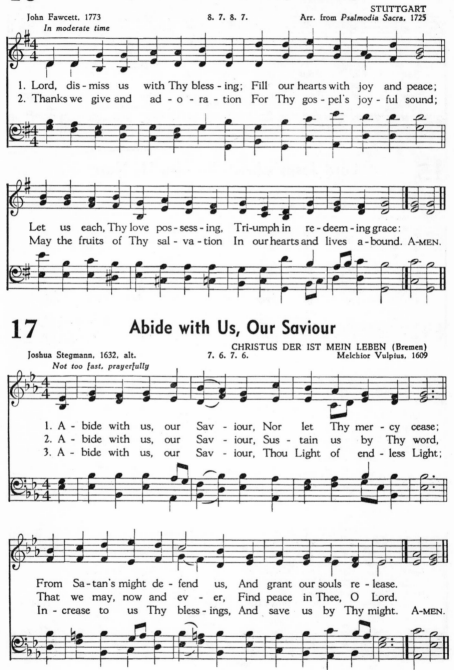

1. Lord, dis-miss us with Thy bless-ing; Fill our hearts with joy and peace;
2. Thanks we give and ad-o-ra-tion For Thy gos-pel's joy-ful sound;

Let us each, Thy love pos-sess-ing, Tri-umph in re-deem-ing grace:
May the fruits of Thy sal-va-tion In our hearts and lives a-bound. A-MEN.

17   Abide with Us, Our Saviour

CHRISTUS DER IST MEIN LEBEN (Bremen)
Joshua Stegmann, 1632, alt.   7. 6. 7. 6.   Melchior Vulpius, 1609

Not too fast, prayerfully

1. A-bide with us, our Sav-iour, Nor let Thy mer-cy cease;
2. A-bide with us, our Sav-iour, Sus-tain us by Thy word,
3. A-bide with us, our Sav-iour, Thou Light of end-less Light;

From Sa-tan's might de-fend us, And grant our souls re-lease.
That we may, now and ev-er, Find peace in Thee, O Lord.
In-crease to us Thy bless-ings, And save us by Thy might. A-MEN.

18 Alleluia, Fairest Morning

GOTT DES HIMMELS UND DER ERDEN (Albert)

Johann Krause, 1739
Tr. Jane Borthwick, 1858

8. 7. 8. 7. 7. 7.

Heinrich Albert, 1643

Joyously

1. Al - le - lu - ia, fair - est morn - ing, Fair - er than our
2. In the glad - ness of His wor - ship We will seek our
3. Let the day with Thee be end - ed, As with Thee it

words can say! Down we lay the heav - y bur - den
joy to - day; It is then we learn the ful - ness
has be - gun, And Thy bless - ing, Lord, be grant - ed,

Of life's toil and care to - day, While this morn of
Of the grace for which we pray, When the word of
Till earth's days and weeks are done; That at last Thy

joy and love Brings fresh vig - or from a - bove.
life is given, Like the Sav - iour's voice from heaven.
serv - ants may Keep e - ter - nal Sab - bath - day. A - MEN.

(17)

19 Light of Light, Enlighten Me

Benjamin Schmolck, 1715
Tr. Catherine Winkworth, 1858

7. 8. 7. 8. 7. 7.

MEINEN JESUM LASS ICH NICHT
Johann Ulich, 1674

In moderate time

1. Light of Light, en-light-en me, Now a-new the
2. Fount of all our joy and peace, To Thy liv-ing
3. Kin-dle Thou the sac-ri-fice That up-on my
4. Let me with my heart to-day, Ho-ly, Ho-ly,

day is dawn-ing; Sun of grace, the shad-ows flee,
wa-ters lead me; Thou from earth my soul re-lease,
lips is ly-ing; Clear the shad-ows from mine eyes,
Ho-ly, sing-ing, Rapt a-while from earth a-way,

Bright-en Thou my Sab-bath morn-ing; With Thy joy-ous
And with grace and mer-cy feed me. Bless Thy word, that
That, from ev-ery er-ror fly-ing, No strange fire may
All my soul to Thee up-spring-ing, Have a fore-taste,

sun-shine blest, Hap-py is my day of rest.
it may prove Rich in fruits that Thou dost love.
in me glow That Thine al-tar doth not know.
in-ly given, How they wor-ship Thee in heaven. A-MEN.

20 Another Six Days' Work Is Done

Rev. Joseph Stennett. 1732   8. 8. 8. 8. 4.   Nikolaus Hermann, 1561

Joyously

1. An - oth - er six days' work is done, An - oth - er Sab-bath is be - gun; Re - turn, my
2. Come, bless the Lord, whose love assigns So sweet a rest to wearied minds; Pro-vides an
3. O that our tho'ts and thanks may rise As grate-ful in-cense to the skies; And draw from
4. In ho - ly du - ties let the day, In ho - ly pleas-ures pass a - way; How sweet a

soul, en - joy the rest, Im-prove the day thy God hath blest. Al - le - lu - ia.
an - te-past to heav'n, And gives this day the food of sev'n. Al - le - lu - ia.
heav'n that sweet re-pose Which none but he that feels it knows. Al - le - lu - ia.
Sab - bath thus to spend In hope of one that ne'er shall end! Al - le - lu - ia! A-MEN.

21 This Is the Day of Light

SWABIA
Johann M. Spiess
Davids Harpffen-Spiel, Heidelberg, 1745
Arr. W. H. Havergal, 1847

John Ellerton, 1867   S. M.

In moderate time

1. This is the day of light: Let there be light to - day;
2. This is the day of rest: Our fail - ing strength re - new;
3. This is the day of peace: Thy peace our spir - its fill;
4. This is the day of prayer: Let earth to heaven draw near;

O Day-spring, rise up - on our night And chase its gloom a - way.
On wea - ry brain and trou-bled breast Shed Thou Thy fresh-ening dew.
Bid Thou the blasts of dis - cord cease, The waves of strife be still.
Lift up our hearts to seek Thee there, Come down to meet us here. A-MEN.

22
My Heart with Joy Now Raises

Author unknown
Tr. based on Catherine Winkworth, 1863   7. 6. 7. 6. 6. 7. 7. 6.

AUS MEINES HERZENS GRUNDE
Gesangbüchlein, Hamburg, 1598

Majestically

1. My heart with joy now rais - es In this fair morn-ing hour A song of
2. For Thou from me hast ward - ed All per - ils of the night; From ev - 'ry
3. Let not Thy mer - cy leave me While here on earth I stay Let noth-ing

thank-ful prais - es To Thine al-might-y pow'r, O God up-on Thy throne, To hon-or
harm hast guard-ed My soul till morning light. To Thee I hum-bly cry, O Sav-iour,
e'er de - ceive me Nor lead my soul a-stray. To Thee, for-ev - er blest, Will I with

and a - dore Thee, I bring my praise be-fore Thee Thru' Christ, Thine on-ly Son.
have com-pas - sion And pardon my trans-gres-sion; Have mer-cy, Lord most high!
mine con - fide me, And will-ing let Thee guide me As seem-eth to me best. A-MEN.

23
Dayspring of Eternity

Christian Knorr von Rosenroth, 1684
Tr. John Henry Hopkins, 1866   7. 8. 7. 8. 7. 3.

MORGENGLANZ DER EWIGKEIT
Freylinghausen's *Gesangbuch*, Halle, 1704

In moderate time

1. Day-spring of E - ter - ni - ty, Bright-ness of the Fa - ther's glo - ry,
2. Let Thy grace like morn-ing dew Fall on hearts in Thee con - fid - ing;
3. Lead us to the gold-en shore, O Thou ris-ing Sun of Morn - ing;

Dawn on us, that we may see Clouds and dark-ness flee be-
Thy sweet com-fort, ev-er new, Fill our souls with strength a-
Lead where tears shall flow no more, Where all sighs to songs are

fore Thee; Drive a-far with con-quering might All our night.
bid-ing; And Thy quicken-ing eyes be-hold Thy dear fold.
turn-ing, Where Thy glo-ry sheds al-way Per-fect day. A-MEN.

EVENING

24   As Fades the Daylight Splendor

NUN RUHEN ALLE WÄLDER (Innsbruck)
Ewald Kockritz, 1916, alt.   7. 7. 6. 7. 7. 8.   Heinrich Isaak, c. 1455-1517
With graceful rhythm

1. As fades the day-light splen-dor, We crave Thy mer-cies ten-der,
2. Thy grace is all pre-vail-ing, Thy mer-cy nev-er-fail-ing,
3. Some-times the way seems drear-y, And weak-ness makes us wear-y:
4. Lord Je-sus who dost love us, Thy pin-ions spread a-bove us,

Thou Lord of Life and Light; Thy love for us a-bound-ing, Thy
E'en though our need is great. Though tri-als hard as-sail us, Thy
Do Thou then make us strong; That, pain and grief con-trol-ling, We
And drive all fear a-way; And when this life is end-ed, By

strong arms, us sur-round-ing, De-fend and shield us through the night.
grace shall nev-er fail us If, trust-ful, we Thy help a-wait.
look for Thy con-sol-ing; For Thou wilt nev-er tar-ry long.
an-gel hosts at-tend-ed Bring us to Thine E-ter-nal Day. A-MEN.

(21)

25 O God, Thou Faithful God

Johann Heermann, 1630
Tr. Catherine Winkworth, 1858, alt.   6. 7. 6. 7. 6. 6. 6. 6.

O GOTT, DU FROMMER GOTT (Darmstadt)
J. G. C. Störl, 1710

In moderate time

1. O God, Thou faith-ful God, Thou foun-tain ev-er flow-ing,
2. Grant Thou me strength to do With read-y heart and will-ing
3. Oh, let me nev-er speak What bounds of truth ex-ceed-eth;
4. If dan-gers gath-er round, Still keep me calm and fear-less;

Who good and per-fect gifts In mer-cy art be-stow-ing,
What-e'er Thou shalt com-mand, My call-ing here ful-fill-ing;
Grant that no i-dle word From out my mouth pro-ceed-eth;
Help me to bear the cross When life is dark and cheer-less;

Give me a health-y frame, And may I have with-in
To do it when I ought, With all my might, and bless
And then, when in my place I must and ought to speak,
And let me win my foe With words and ac-tions kind.

A con-science free from blame, A soul un-hurt by sin!
The work I thus have wrought, For Thou must give suc-cess.
My words grant pow'r and grace Lest I of-fend the weak.
When coun-sel I would know, Good coun-sel let me find. A-MEN.

26   How Great Thy Goodness

Chr. F. Gellert, 1715-1769
Tr. Rev. C. G. Haas, 1898   9. 8. 9. 8. D.   GELLERT
                                          Chr. Friedr. Richter, 1703

Majestically

1. How great Thy good-ness, heav'nly Fa-ther!   Is   he   a man that ev - er feels,
2. Who hath in heav'n-ly wis-dom made me?   Thou God, who art om-nip-o - tent.
3. Look, O   my soul, in - to yon re-gions   To which thy Ma - ker call - eth thee;
4. O   God, dis - play Thy lov - ing-kind-ness   My grand-est vi - sion e'er to be;

Thy   count-less mer - cies round him gath-er,   And yet no grat - i - tude re - veals?
Who   hath by pa - tient guid-ance led me?   The One whose counsel brings con-tent.
When thou with glo - rious, hap - py le-gions   Thy God for - ev - er clear shalt see.
To strength-en all   my good im - puls - es,   My life and all to give to Thee;

O   that my high - est du - ty ev - er   Be   this, to   fath-om His deep love!
Who giv - eth peace to trou-bled conscience, Who fills my   heart with hope di-vine
Re - joic - ing sweet be - yond is of - fered, To   ev - er - y soul e - ter - nal life,
Thy love my com-fort when I lan-guish, My   guide in   days of sun-shine clear;

The Lord hath me for-got - ten nev - er,   Praise thou, my soul, the Lord a - bove.
And drives a - way the fear of vengeance? 'Tis His strong arm and grace sub-lime.
Since Je-sus Christ, the Sav-iour, suf-fered   And rose, the Vic - tor in the strife.
In death's approach, the fi - nal an-guish, Al - lay all doubt, dis - pel all fear. A-MEN.

27 O How Shall I Receive Thee

VALET WILL ICH DIR GEBEN (st. theodulph)
7. 6. 7. 6. D.

Paul Gerhardt, 1653

Melchior Teschner, 1615

In march rhythm

1. O how shall I re - ceive Thee, How meet Thee on Thy way,
2. Thy Zi - on palms is strew - ing, And branch - es fresh and fair;
3. Love caused Thy in - car - na - tion, Love brought Thee down to me;
4. He who a - lone can cheer you Is stand - ing at the door;

Blest hope of ev - ery na - tion, My soul's de - light and stay?
My soul, in praise a - wak - ing, Her an - them shall pre - pare.
Thy thirst for my sal - va - tion Pro - cured my lib - er - ty.
He brings His pi - ty near you, And bids you weep no more.

O Je - sus, Je - sus, give me Now by Thine own pure light,
Per - pet - ual thanks and prais - es Forth from my heart shall spring;
O love be - yond all tell - ing, That led Thee to em - brace,
He comes, who con - trite sin - ners Will with the chil - dren place,

To know what-e'er is pleas - ing And wel - come in Thy sight.
And to Thy name the serv - ice Of all my powers I bring.
In love all love ex - cel - ling, Our lost and fall - en race!
The chil - dren of His Fa - ther, The heirs of life and grace. A - MEN.

28 Comfort, Comfort Ye My People

John Olearius, 1671
Tr. Catherine Winkworth, 1862   8. 7. 8. 7. 7. 7. 8. 8.

WERDE MUNTER, MEIN GEMÜTE
Johann Schop, 1642

In graceful rhythm

1. Com - fort, com - fort ye my peo - ple, Speak ye peace, thus saith our God;
2. For the her - ald's voice is cry - ing In the des - ert far and near,
3. Make ye straight what long was crook-ed, Make the rough - er pla - ces plain:

Com - fort those who sit in dark-ness, Mourn-ing 'neath their sor - rows' load.
Bid - ding all men to re - pent-ance. Since the king-dom now is here.
Let your hearts be true and hum - ble, As be - fits His ho - ly reign;

Speak ye to Je - ru - sa - lem Of the peace that waits for them;
O, that warn - ing cry o - bey, Now pre - pare for God a - way!
For the glo - ry of the Lord Now o'er earth is shed a - broad,

Tell her that her sins I cov - er, And her war - fare now is o - ver.
Let the val - leys rise to meet Him And the hills bow down to greet Him.
And all flesh shall see the to - ken That His word is nev - er bro-ken. A-MEN.

29 Arise, the Kingdom Is at Hand

ELLACOMBE

Johann Rist, 1651
Tr. Catherine Winkworth, 1858

C. M. D.

Gesangbuch der Herzogl. Wirtembergischen
Katholischen Hofkapelle, 1784

In marked rhythm

1. A - rise, the king-dom is at hand, The King is draw-ing nigh;
2. Look up, ye droop-ing hearts, to - day, The King is ver - y near;
3. O rich the gifts Thou bring-est us, Thy - self made poor and weak;

A - rise with joy, thou faith-ful band, To meet the Lord most high!
O cast your griefs and fears a - way, For, lo, your help is here!
O love be - yond com - pare that thus Can foes and sin - ners seek!

Look up, ye souls weighed down with care, The Sov-ereign is not far;
Hope on, ye bro - ken hearts, at last The King comes in His might;
For this we raise a glad - some voice On high to Thee a - lone,

Look up, faint hearts, from your de - spair, Be - hold the Morn-ing Star!
He loved us in the a - ges past, When we lay wrapped in night.
And ev - er - more with thanks re - joice Be - fore Thy glo-rious throne. A-MEN.

30 Lift Up Your Heads, Ye Mighty Gates

Georg Weissel, 1642
Tr. Catherine Winkworth, 1855   8. 8. 8. 8. 8. 8. 6. 6.

MACHT HOCH DIE TÜR
J. A. Freylinghausen, 1704

Joyfully; not too slowly

1. Lift up your heads, ye might-y gates, Be-hold the King of glo-ry waits;
2. The Lord is just, a Help-er tried, Mer-cy is ev-er at His side;
3. O blest the land, the cit-y blest, Where Christ the Rul-er is con-fessed!
4. Fling wide the por-tals of your heart; Make it a tem-ple, set a-part

The King of kings is draw-ing near, The Sav-iour of the world is here;
His king-ly crown is ho-li-ness, His scep-ter, pit-y in dis-tress;
O hap-py hearts and hap-py homes To whom this King in tri-umph comes!
From earth-ly use for heaven's em-ploy, A-dorned with prayer, and love, and joy;

Life and sal-va-tion He doth bring, Where-fore re-joice and glad-ly sing:
The end of all our woe He brings; Where-fore the earth is glad and sings:
The cloud-less Sun of joy He is, Who bring-eth pure de-light and bliss:
So shall your Sov-ereign en-ter in, And new and no-bler life be-gin:

We praise Thee, Fa-ther, now, Cre-a-tor, wise art Thou!
We praise Thee, Sav-iour, now, Might-y in-deed art Thou!
O Com-fort-er di-vine, What bound-less grace is Thine!
To Thee, O God, be praise For word and deed and grace! A-MEN.

31 Wake, Awake, for Night Is Flying

Philipp Nicolai, 1599
Tr. Catherine Winkworth, 1858, alt.

WACHET AUF
Philipp Nicolai, 1599

8. 9. 8. 8. 9. 8. 6. 6. 4. 4. 4. 8.

With spirit

1. Wake, a-wake, for night is fly - ing, The watch-men on the heights are cry - ing,
2. Zi - on hears the watch-men sing - ing, Her heart with deep de - light is spring-ing,
3. Now let all the heavens a - dore Thee, And men and an - gels sing be - fore Thee

A - wake, Je - ru - sa - lem, a - rise! Mid-night's sol-emn hour is toll - ing,
She wakes, she ris - es from her gloom; For her Lord comes down all glo - rious,
With harp and cym - bal's clear-est tone; Of one pearl each shin - ing por - tal,

His char - iot wheels are near - er roll - ing; He comes, O Church, lift up thine eyes!
In grace ar-rayed, by truth vic - to - rious; Her Star is risen, her Light is come!
Where we shall join the choirs im - mor - tal In prais - es round Thy glo-rious throne;

Rise up, with will - ing feet Go forth, the Bride-groom meet: Hal - le - lu - jah!
Ah, come Thou bless - ed One, God's own be - lov - ed Son, Hal - le - lu - jah!
No vi - sion ev - er brought, No ear hath ev - er caught Such great glo - ry!

(28)

Wake, Awake, for Night Is Flying

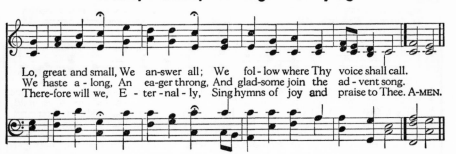

Lo, great and small, We an-swer all; We fol-low where Thy voice shall call.
We haste a-long, An ea-ger throng, And glad-some join the ad-vent song.
There-fore will we, E - ter-nal-ly, Sing hymns of joy and praise to Thee. A-MEN.

32   Hark, the Glad Sound, the Saviour Comes

LOBT GOTT IHR CHRISTEN ALLZUGLEICH (HERMANN)
C. M.

Philip Doddridge, 1735   Nicolaus Hermann, 1554

Joyfully

1. Hark, the glad sound, the Sav - iour comes, The Sav - iour
2. He comes the pris - oners to re - lease, In Sa - tan's
3. He comes, the bro - ken heart to bind, The bleed - ing
4. Our glad ho - san - nas, Prince of Peace, Thy wel - come

prom - ised long: Let ev - ery heart pre - pare a throne, And
bond - age held: The gates of brass be - fore Him burst, The
soul to cure, And would with treas - ures of His grace En -
shall pro - claim; And heaven's e - ter - nal arch - es ring With

ev - ery voice a song, And ev - ery voice a song.
i - ron fet - ters yield, The i - ron fet - ters yield.
rich the hum - ble poor, En - rich the hum - ble poor.
Thy be - lov - ed name, With Thy be - lov - ed name. A-MEN.

33 From Heaven Above to Earth I Come

Martin Luther, 1535
Tr. Catherine Winkworth, 1855   L. M.   VOM HIMMEL HOCH (Erfurt)
                                                       Geistliche Lieder, Leipzig, 1539

In graceful rhythm

1. From heaven a - bove to earth I come, To bear good news to ev - ery home;
2. "To you, this night, is born a Child Of Ma - ry, cho - sen moth - er mild;
3. "'Tis Christ, our God, who far on high Hath heard your sad and bit - ter cry;
4. Wel - come to earth, Thou no - ble Guest, Thro' whom e'en wick-ed men are blest!
5. Ah, dear - est Je - sus, Ho - ly Child, Make Thee a bed, soft, un - de - filed,
6. Glo - ry to God in high-est heaven, Who un - to man His Son hath given,

Glad ti - dings of great joy I bring, Where-of I now will say and sing:
This lit - tle Child of low - ly birth, Shall be the joy of all the earth."
Him - self will your sal - va - tion be, Him-self from sin will make you free."
Thou comest to share our mis - er - y; What can we ren - der, Lord, to Thee?
With - in my heart, that it may be A qui - et cham-ber kept for Thee.
While an - gels sing with pi - ous mirth A glad New Year to all the earth. A-MEN.

34 All My Heart this Night Rejoices

Paul Gerhardt, 1656
Tr. Catherine Winkworth, 1858   WARUM SOLLT ICH MICH DENN GRÄMEN (Bonn)
                                 8. 3. 3. 6. D.   Johann Georg Ebeling, 1666

Joyously

1. All my heart this night re - joic - es, As I hear, far and near,
2. Hark, a voice from yon - der man - ger, Soft and sweet, doth en - treat,
3. Come, then, let us has - ten yon - der; Here let all, great and small,

Sweet - est an - gel voi - ces; "Christ is born," their choirs are sing - ing,
"Flee from woe and dan - ger; Breth - ren, come! from all that grieves you
Kneel in awe and won - der; Love Him who with love is yearn - ing;

All My Heart this Night Rejoices

Till the air ev-'ry-where Now with joy is ring - ing.
You are freed; all you need I will sure - ly give you."
Hail the star that from far Bright with hope is burn - ing! A-MEN.

35 Behold a Branch Is Growing

Sixteenth Century
Tr. st. 1-4, Harriet R. Krauth, 1875
St. 5, John Caspar Mattes, 1914

ES IST EIN REIS ENTSPRUNGEN
Traditional Rhenish Folk Song
Alte Kath. Geistliche Kirchengesäng, Köln, 1599
7. 6. 7. 6. 6. 7. 6.

With joy and dignity

1. Be - hold a Branch is grow-ing Of love-liest form and grace; As proph-ets
2. I - sa - iah hath fore-told it In words of prom-ise sure, And Ma-ry's
3. The shep-herds heard the sto - ry Pro-claimed by an-gels bright, How Christ, the
4. This Flower, whose fra-grance ten-der With sweet-ness fills the air, Dis - pels with
5. O Sav-iour, Child of Ma - ry, Who felt our hu-man woe, O Sav-iour,

sung, fore-know-ing, It springs from Jes-se's race, And bears one lit - tle Flower
arms en - fold It, A vir - gin meek and pure. Thru God's e - ter - nal will
Lord of glo - ry Was born on earth this night. To Beth - le - hem they sped,
glo - rious splen-dor The dark-ness ev - ery-where. True Man, yet ver - y God,
King of glo - ry, Who dost our weak-ness know, Bring us at length we pray

In midst of cold - est win - ter, At deep-est mid-night hour.
This Child to her is giv - en, At mid-night calm and still.
And in the man-ger found Him, As an - gel - her - alds said.
From sin and death He saves us And light-ens ev - er - y load.
To the bright courts of heav - en, And to the end - less day. A - MEN.

36 O Sacred Head, Now Wounded

HERZLICH TUT MICH VERLANGEN (Passion Chorale)
Ascribed to Bernard of Clairvaux, 1091-1153
Tr. Paul Gerhardt, 1656; tr. J. W. Alexander, 1830
Hans Leo Hassler, 1601
Har. Joh. Sebastian Bach, 1729

7. 6. 7. 6. D.

With great dignity

1. O Sa - cred Head, now wound - ed, With grief and shame weighed down,
2. What Thou, my Lord, hast suf - fered Was all for sin - ners' gain:
3. What lan - guage shall I bor - row To thank Thee, dear - est Friend,
4. When strength one day shall fail me, Lord, fail me not, I pray:

Now scorn - ful - ly sur - round - ed With thorns, Thine on - ly crown;
Mine, mine was the trans - gres - sion, But Thine the dead - ly pain.
For this Thy dy - ing sor - row, Thy pit - y with - out end?
When pangs of death as - sail me, Be - side me, Je - sus, stay:

O Sa - cred Head, what glo - ry, What bliss till now was Thine!
Lo, here I fall, my Sav - iour, 'Tis I de - serve Thy place;
O make me Thine for - ev - er; And should I faint - ing be,
When, head and heart, I lan - guish, And hard - ly draw my breath,

Yet, though de - spised and go - ry, I joy to call Thee mine!
Look on me with Thy fa - vor, Vouch-safe to me Thy grace.
Lord, let me nev - er, nev - er Out - live my love to Thee.
De - liv - er me from an - guish, By vir - tue of Thy death. A-MEN.

37 Jesus, Refuge of the Weary

Girolamo Savonarola, 1452-1498
Tr. Jane Francesca Wilde, 1826-1896

ALLE MENSCHEN MÜSSEN STERBEN (Darmstadt)
8. 7. 8. 7. 8. 8. 7. 7.
H. Müller, 1687

In moderate time

1. Je - sus, ref - uge of the wea - ry, Ob - ject of the spir - it's love,
2. Do we pass that cross un - heed - ing, Breath - ing no re - pent - ant vow,
3. Je - sus, may our hearts be burn - ing With more fer - vant love for Thee;

Foun - tain in life's des - ert drear - y, Sav - iour from the world a - bove,
Though we see Thee wound - ed, bleed - ing, See Thy thorn - en - cir - cled brow?
May our eyes be ev - er turn - ing To Thy cross of ag - o - ny;

Though Thy heart was oft of - fend - ed, E'en up - on the cross ex - tend - ed
Yet Thy won - drous grace hath taught us What Thy sin - less death hath brought us,
Till in glo - ry, part - ed nev - er, One with Thee in love for - ev - er,

Thou didst mourn the sin - ners' fall, And didst bear the pain of all.
Life e - ter - nal, peace, and rest On the gen - tle Sav - iour's breast.
At the bless - ed Sav - iour's side We u - nit - ed shall a - bide. A-MEN.

38 Man of Sorrows, Now My Soul Shall Greet Thee

C. R. von Zinzendorf, 1727-1762
Tr. J. C. Hansen, 1916 10 7. 10. 7. 10. 10. 7. 7. MARTER CHRISTI
Gnadauer Choralbuch, 1735

Rather slowly and solemnly

1. Man of Sor - rows, now my soul shall greet Thee, Pa - tient Suf - ferer,
2. Thou - sand thanks, Thou Soul so true and ten - der, Thou hast brought the
3. At Thy cross my trou - bled heart finds ref - uge, To Thy pierc - ed
4. All of us who here have come to - geth - er Join our hands in

crowned with thorns; There on Cal - vary's height, O Lord, I'll meet Thee
sac - ri - fice! All my heart and soul shall wor - ship ren - der,
side it flees; 'Mid the storm of life and sin's drear del - uge
u - ni - ty; To the cross of Christ our souls we'll teth - er,

At the cross the world still scorns; There I see the Lamb that,
That Thou paid'st in full the price! Ev - ery tongue shall tell re -
Let it rest with Thee in peace; And when death's dark shad - ows
Faith - ful un - to death we'll be. But Thou, bless - ed Lord in

un - com - plain - ing, Suf - fers for us all, our par - don gain - ing:
demp-tion's sto - ry, Ev - ery knee shall bend to Thee in glo - ry,
shall en - fold me, Then, O Cru - ci - fied, let me be - hold Thee;
high - est heav - en, Hear the prom - is - es that we have giv - en;

Man of Sorrows, Now My Soul Shall Greet Thee

Noth - ing shall more pre-cious be Than the Cru - ci - fied to me.
Where, with those saved by Thy grace, I shall see Thee face to face.
In - to Thine al - might - y hand, Lord, my spir - it I com-mend.
"A - men, A - men," sweet-ly call, "A - men, Peace be with you all." A-MEN.

Words copyright, 1941, Eden Publishing House.

39 Ah, Dearest Jesus, How Hast Thou Offended

Johann Heermann, c. 1630
Tr. Robert Bridges, 1899   11. 11. 11. 5.   HERZLIEBSTER JESU
Johann Crüger, 1640

Rather slowly and solemnly
May be sung in unison

1. Ah, dear - est Je - sus, how hast Thou of - fend - ed,
2. Who was the guilt - y? Who brought this up - on Thee?
3. For me, dear Je - sus, was Thy in - car - na - tion,
4. There - fore, dear Je - sus, since I can - not pay Thee,

That man to judge Thee hath in hate pre - tend - ed? By foes de -
A - las, my trea - son, Je - sus, hath un - done Thee! 'Twas I, Lord
Thy mor - tal sor - row, and Thy life's ob - la - tion; Thy death of
I do a - dore Thee, and will ev - er pray Thee, Think on Thy

rid - ed, by Thine own re - ject - ed, O most af - flict - ed!
Je - sus, I it was de - nied Thee: I cru - ci - fied Thee.
an - guish and Thy bit - ter pas - sion, For my sal - va - tion.
pit - y and Thy love un-swerv - ing, Not my de - serv - ing. A-MEN.

(35)

40 Christ, the Life of All the Living

Ernst Christian Homburg, 1659
Tr. Catherine Winkworth, 1851, alt. 8. 7. 8. 7. 8. 8. 7. 7.
GÜTERSLOH
Lüneburgisches Gesangbuch, 1661

Not too slowly

1. Christ, the life of all the liv - ing, Christ, the death of death, our foe,
2. Thou, ah, Thou hast ta - ken on Thee Bit - ter strokes, a cru - el rod;
3. Thou didst bear the smit - ing, on - ly That it might not fall on me;
4. Then for all that wrought our par - don, For Thy sor - row deep and sore,

Who, Thy - self for us once giv - ing To the dark - ened depths of woe;
Pain and scorn was heaped up - on Thee, O Thou sin - less Son of God;
Thou stoodst false - ly charged and lone - ly That I might be safe and free;
For Thine an - guish in the gar - den I will thank Thee ev - er - more;

In - to ut - ter des - o - la - tion Thou didst go for our sal - va - tion;
Thro' Thy hands the nails were driv - en That I might have free - dom giv - en;
Thy soul cried by God for - sa - ken That my faith might ne'er be sha - ken;
For the words that Thou hast spo - ken Ere thy gen - tle heart was bro - ken:

Thou-sand, thou-sand thanks shall be, Bless-ed Je - sus, un - to Thee! A-MEN.

41 Christ, Thou Blest Redeemer

Rev. R. A. John, 1912   6. 7. 5. 6. 7. 5. 6. 7. 6. 2.   LAMM GOTTES
Anon.

May be sung in unison

Christ, Thou blest Re- deem- er, Thou hast borne our sins a - way;

Lord, we a - dore Thee; Christ, Thou bless - ed Sav - iour,

Thou hast made our spir - its whole; Lord, we a - dore Thee;

Christ, Thou bless - ed Mas - ter, Thou hast called us to Thy heart;

Bless us, we im - plore Thee. A - - - - - men.

42   Jesus Lives and So Shall I

Christian F. Gellert, 1715-1769
Tr. Anon.

JESUS MEINE ZUVERSICHT (Ratisbon)
From Johann Crüger's
7. 8. 7. 8. 7. 7.   *Praxis Pietatis Melica, c. 1653*

Jubilantly

1. Je - sus lives and so shall I; Death, thy sting is
2. Je - sus lives, and God ex - tends Grace to each re-
3. Je - sus lives, and by His grace Vic - tory o'er my
4. Je - sus lives, and death is now But my en - try

gone for - ev - er. He who deigned for me to die
turn - ing sin - ner. Reb - els He re - ceives as friends,
pas - sions giv - ing, I will cleanse my heart and ways,
in - to glo - ry. Cour - age, then, my soul, for thou

Lives the bands of death to sev - er. He shall raise me
And ex - alts to high - est hon - or. God is true as
Ev - er to His glo - ry liv - ing. Th'weak He rais - es
Hast a crown of life be - fore thee; Thou shalt find Thy

with the just: Je - sus is my hope and trust.
He is just: Je - sus is my hope and trust.
from the dust: Je - sus is my hope and trust.
hopes were just: Je - sus is my hope and trust. A - MEN.

43 Hail the Day that Sees Him Rise

Charles Wesley, 1739

GOTT SEI DANK DURCH ALLE WELT
7. 7. 7. 7.   Freylinghausen's *Gesangbuch*, Halle, 1704

May be sung in unison

1. Hail the day that sees Him rise, To His throne a - bove the skies!
2. There the glo - rious tri - umph waits: Lift your heads, e - ter - nal gates,
3. Him though high-est heaven re - ceives, Still He loves the world He leaves;

Christ, a while to mor - tals given, Re - as - cends His na - tive heaven.
Wide un - fold the ra-diant scene, Take the King of Glo - ry in!
Though re - turn-ing to His throne, Still He calls man - kind His own. A-MEN.

44 Majestic Sweetness Sits Enthroned

Samuel Stennett, 1787

C. M.

NUN DANKET ALL (Gräfenberg)
Johann Crüger, 1656

Not too fast; with feeling

1. Ma - jes - tic sweet-ness sits en - throned Up - on the Sav-iour's brow;
2. No mor - tal can with Him com - pare A - mong the sons of men;
3. To Him I owe my life and breath, And all the joys I have;
4. To heaven, the place of His a - bode He brings my wea - ry feet;
5. Since from His boun - ty I re - ceive Such proofs of love di - vine,

His head with ra - diant glo - ries crowned, His lips with grace o'er - flow.
Fair - er is He than all the fair That fill the heaven - ly train.
He makes me tri - umph o - ver death, And saves me from the grave.
Shows me the glo - ries of my God, And makes my joys com - plete.
Had I a thou-sand hearts to give, Lord, they should all be Thine. A-MEN.

(39)

45
O Holy Spirit, Enter In

WIE SCHÖN LEUCHTET (Frankfort)

Michael Schirmer, 1640
Tr. Catherine Winkworth, 1862   8. 8. 7. 8. 8. 7. 8. 4. 4. 8.   Philipp Nicolai, 1599

In moderate time; reverently

1. O Ho-ly Spir-it, en-ter in, A-mong these hearts Thy work be-gin,
2. Left to our-selves, we shall but stray; O lead us in the nar-row way,
3. O might-y Rock, O Source of Life, Let Thy dear word 'mid doubt and strife
4. Grant that our days, while life shall last, In pur-est ho-li-ness be passed;

Thy tem-ple deign to make us; Sun of the soul, Thou Light di-vine,
With wis-est coun-sel guide us; And give us stead-fast-ness, that we
Be so with-in us burn-ing, That we be faith-ful un-to death,
Our minds so rule and strength-en That they may rise o'er things of earth,

A-round and in us bright-ly shine, To strength and glad-ness wake us.
May hence-forth tru-ly fol-low Thee, What-ev-er woes be-tide us:
In Thy pure love and ho-ly faith, From Thee true wis-dom learn-ing!
The hopes and joys that here have birth; And if our course Thou lengh-en,

Where Thou shin-est, life from heav-en There is giv-en;
Heal Thou gen-tly hearts now bro-ken, Give some to-ken
Lord, Thy gra-ces on us show-er; By Thy pow-er
Keep Thou pure, Lord, from of-fen-ses, Heart and sen-ses;

O Holy Spirit, Enter in

We be - fore Thee For that pre-cious gift im - plore Thee.
Thou art near us, Whom we trust to light and cheer us.
Christ con - fess - ing, Let us win His grace and bless - ing.
Bless - ed Spir - it, Bid us thus true life in - her - it. A-MEN.

46   Come, O Come, Thou Quickening Spirit

Henry Held, d. 1659
Tr. Charles William Schaeffer, 1866   8. 7. 8. 7. 7. 7.   Joh. Christoph Bach, 1680

EISENACH

In moderate time

1. Come, O come, Thou quick-'ning Spir - it, Thou for - ev - er art di - vine;
2. Grant my mind and my af - fec - tions Wis - dom, coun - sel, pu - ri - ty;
3. Ho - ly Spir - it, strong and might - y, Thou who mak - est all things new,
4. In the faith O make me sted - fast; Let not Sa - tan, death, or shame

Let Thy pow - er nev - er fail me, Al - ways fill this heart of mine;
That I may be ev - er seek - ing Naught but that which pleas - es Thee.
Make Thy work with - in me per - fect, Help me by Thy word so true,
Of my con - fi - dence de - prive me; Lord, my ref - uge is Thy name.

Thus shall grace, and truth, and light Dis - si - pate the gloom of night.
Let Thy knowl-edge spread and grow, Work-ing er - ror's o - ver-throw.
Arm me with that sword of Thine, And the vic-t'ry shall be mine.
When the flesh in - clines to ill, Let Thy word prove stronger still. A-MEN.

47 We All Believe in One True God

The Nicene Creed
Wir glauben all' an *einen* Gott
Martin Luther, 1525
Tr. composite

8. 8. 8. 8. 8. 8. 8. 8. 8. 8.

WIR GLAUBEN ALL' AN EINEN GOTT
Manuskript Gesangbuch
Langenöls, 1742

In majestic style

1. We all be-lieve in one true God, Who cre-at-ed earth and heav-en,
2. We all be-lieve in Je-sus Christ, His own Son, our Lord, pos-sess-ing
3. We all con-fess the Ho-ly Ghost, Who sweet grace and com-fort giv-eth

The Fa-ther, who to us in love Hath the right of chil-dren giv-en.
An e-qual Godhead, throne, and might, Source of ev-'ry grace and bless-ing.
And with the Fa-ther and the Son In e-ter-nal glo-ry liv-eth;

He both soul and bod-y feed-eth, All we need He doth pro-vide us;
Born of Ma-ry, vir-gin moth-er, By the pow-er of the Spir-it,
Who the Church, His own cre-a-tion, Keeps in u-ni-ty of spir-it.

He thro' snares and per-ils lead-eth, Watch-ing that no harm be-tide us.
Made true man, our eld-er Broth-er, That the lost might life in-her-it;
Here for-give-ness and sal-va-tion Dai-ly come thro' Je-sus' mer-it.

We All Believe in One True God

He car-eth for us day and night, All things are gov-erned by His might.
Was cru-ci-fied for sin-ful men And raised by God to life a-gain.
All flesh shall rise, and we shall be In bliss with God e-ter-nal-ly. A-MEN.

48 Praise Ye the Father

Elizabeth Charles | 11. 11. 11. 5. | INTEGER VITÆ (Flemming)
Friedrich F. Flemming, 1810

Not too fast; with feeling

1. Praise ye the Fa-ther for His lov-ing kind-ness; Ten-der-ly
2. Praise ye the Sav-iour, great is His com-pas-sion; Gra-cious-ly
3. Praise ye the Spir-it, Com-fort-er of Is-rael, Sent of the

cares He for His err-ing chil-dren; Praise Him, ye an-gels,
cares He for His cho-sen peo-ple; Young men and maid-ens,
Fa-ther and the Son to bless us; Praise ye the Fa-ther,

praise Him in the heav-ens, Praise ye Je-ho-vah.
ye old men and chil-dren, Praise ye the Sav-iour.
Son, and Ho-ly Spir-it, Praise ye the Triune God. A-MEN.

49   Deck Thyself, My Soul, with Gladness

Johann Franck, c. 1649
Tr. Catherine Winkworth, 1863

SCHMÜCKE DICH O LIEBE SEELE (Berlin)
L. M. D.
Johann Crüger, 1649

In moderate time

1. Deck thy-self, my soul, with glad-ness, Leave the gloom-y
2. Has-ten as a bride to meet Him, And with lov-ing
3. Now I sink be-fore Thee low-ly, Filled with joy most
4. Sun, who all my life dost bright-en, Light, who dost my

haunts of sad-ness; Come in-to the day-light's splen-dor,
rev-erence greet Him, For with words of life im-mor-tal
deep and ho-ly, As, with trem-bling awe and won-der,
soul en-light-en, Joy, the sweet-est man e'er know-eth,

There with joy thy prais-es ren-der Un-to Him whose grace un-bound-ed
Now He knock-eth at thy por-tal; O-pen thou the gates be-fore Him,
On Thy might-y works I pon-der; Now by mys-ter-y sur-round-ed,
Fount, whence all my be-ing flow-eth, At Thy feet I fall, my Mak-er,

Hath this won-drous ban-quet found-ed; High o'er all the heavens He
Say-ing, as thou dost a-dore Him: Suf-fer, Lord, that I re-
Depths no man has ev-er sound-ed, None may dare to pierce, un-
Let me be a fit par-tak-er Of this bless-ed food from

Deck Thyself, My Soul, with Gladness

reign - eth, Yet to dwell with thee He deign - eth.
ceive Thee, And I nev - er - more will leave Thee.
bid - den, Se - crets that with Thee are hid - den.
heav - en, In Thy love to mor - tals giv - en. A-MEN.

50   ## O Lamb of God Who, Bleeding

Nicolaus Decius, 1531   **7. 7. 7. 7. 7. 7. 8.**   AGNUS DEI
Nicolaus Decius, 1531

May be sung in unison

O Lamb of God who, bleed - ing, Up - on the cross didst

lan - guish, Nor scorn or mal - ice heed - ing, So pa - tient in Thine

an - guish, On Thee our guilt was ly - - - ing; Thou sav - edst

us by dy - ing: Have mer - cy on us, Lord Je - sus.

51   O Word of God Incarnate

MUNICH
Neuvermehrtes Meiningsches Gesangbuch. 1693

William Walsham How, 1867   **7. 6. 7. 6. D.**   Harmonized by Mendelssohn

With joyous feeling

1. O Word of God In - car - nate, O Wis - dom from on high,
2. The Church from her dear Mas - ter Re - ceived the gift di - vine,
3. It float - eth like a ban - ner Be - fore God's host un - furled;
4. O make Thy Church, dear Sav - iour, A lamp of pur - est gold,

O Truth un-changed, un-chang - ing, O Light of our dark sky;
And still that light she lift - eth O'er all the earth to shine.
It shin - eth like a bea - con A - bove the dark - ling world;
To bear a - mong the na - tions Thy true light as of old.

We praise Thee for the ra - diance That from the hal - lowed page,
It is the gold - en cas - ket Where gems of truth are stored;
It is the chart and com - pass That o'er life's surg - ing sea,
O teach Thy wan-dering pil - grims By this their path to trace,

A lan - tern to our foot - steps, Shines on from age to age.
It is the heaven - drawn pic - ture Of Christ, the liv - ing Word.
'Mid mists, and rocks, and quick-sands Still guides, O Christ, to Thee.
Till, clouds and dark - ness end - ed, They see Thee face to face. A-MEN.

52   Holy Lord, Holy Lord

Christian Gregor. 1723-1801
V. 2. C. G. Clemens
V. 3. J. Swertner   6. 7. 8. 7. 8. 9. 6.   FAHRE FORT
Joh. Eusebius Schmidt, 1704

Joyfully, with dignity

1. Ho - ly Lord, Ho - ly Lord, Ho - ly and Al - might - y Lord,
2. Thanks and praise, thanks and praise, Thanks and praise be ev - er Thine,
3. Lord, our God, Lord, our God, May Thy pre - cious sav - ing word,

Thou, who, as the great Cre - a - tor, Art by all Thy works a - dored;
That Thy word to us is giv - en, Teach-ing us with power di - vine,
Till our race is here com - plet - ed, Light un - to our path af - ford;

Source of u - ni - ver - sal na - ture, And to man, re -
That the Lord of earth and heav - en, Ev - er - last - ing
And, when in Thy pres - ence seat - ed, We to Thee will

deemed by Je - sus' blood. Sov - ereign Good, sov - ereign Good.
life for us to gain, Once was slain, once was slain.
ren - der for Thy grace Cease - less praise, cease - less praise. A - MEN.

53   Out of the Depths I Cry to Thee

Martin Luther, 1523
Tr. as in New Congregational Hymn Book, 1859
8. 7. 8. 7. 8. 8. 7.

AUS TIEFER NOT (Herr, Wie du Willst)
Teutsch Kirchenampt, Strassburg, 1525

With quiet confidence

1. Out of the depths I cry to Thee; Lord, hear me, I implore Thee; Bend down Thy gracious ear to me, Let my prayer come before Thee! On my misdeeds in mercy look, O deign to blot them from Thy book, Or who can stand before Thee?

2. Thy sovereign grace and boundless love Make Thee, O Lord, forgiving; My purest thoughts and deeds but prove, Sin in my heart is living: None guiltless in Thy sight appear, All who approach Thy throne must fear, And humbly trust Thy mercy.

3. Thou canst be merciful whilst just, This is my hope's foundation; On Thy redeeming grace I trust, Grant me, then, Thy salvation. Shielded by Thee, I stand secure; Thy word is firm, Thy promise sure, And I rely upon Thee.

4. Wher-e'er the greatest sins abound, By grace they are exceeded; Thy helping hand is always found With aid, where aid is needed: Thy hand, the only hand to save, Will save the sinner from the grave, And pardon his transgression. A-MEN.

54 Lord, Thy Mercy Now Entreating

Mary Ann Sidebotham, 1881　　　　8. 7. 8. 7.　　　RINGE RECHT (Batty)
Johann Thommen's, *Choralbuch*, 1745

Rather slowly

1. Lord, Thy mer-cy now en-treat-ing, Low be-fore Thy throne we fall;
2. Sin-ful thoughts and words un-lov-ing Rise a-gainst us one by one;
3. Hearts that far from Thee were stray-ing, While in prayer we bowed the knee;
4. Lord, Thy mer-cy still en-treat-ing, We with shame our sins would own;
5. Heaven-ly Fa-ther, bless Thy chil-dren; Heark-en from Thy throne on high;

Our mis-deeds to Thee con-fess-ing, On Thy Name we hum-bly call.
Acts un-wor-thy, deeds un-think-ing, Good that we have left un-done.
Lips that, while Thy prais-es sound-ing, Lift-ed not the soul to Thee.
From hence-forth, the time re-deem-ing, May we live to Thee a-lone.
Lov-ing Sav-iour, Ho-ly Spir-it, Hear and heed our hum-ble cry. A-MEN.

55 Renew Me, O Eternal Light

Erneure mich, o ew'ges Licht
Johann F. Ruopp, 1714, cento
Tr. August Crull, †1923　　　　L. M.
HERR JESU CHRIST, MEIN'S
As Hymnodus Sacer
Leipzig, 1625

Slowly and with dignity

1. Re-new me, O e-ter-nal Light, And let my heart and soul be bright,
2. De-stroy in me the lust of sin, From all im-pure-ness make me clean.
3. Cre-ate in me a new heart, Lord, That glad-ly I o-bey Thy Word
4. Grant that I on-ly Thee may love And seek those things which are a-bove

Il-lu-mined with the light of grace That is-sues from Thy ho-ly face.
Oh, grant me pow'r and strength, my God, To strive a-gainst my flesh and blood!
And naught but what Thou wilt, de-sire; With such new life my soul in-spire.
Till I be-hold Thee face to face, O Light e-ter-nal, thro' Thy grace. A-MEN.

56 If Thou But Suffer God to Guide Thee

WER NUR DEN LIEBEN GOTT LÄSST WALTEN (minor melody)

Georg Neumark, 1641
Tr. Catherine Winkworth, 1855, alt. 9. 8. 9. 8. 8. 8. Georg Neumark, 1657

Slowly and with dignity

1. If thou but suf-fer God to guide thee, And hope in Him thro' all thy ways, He'll give thee strength, what-e'er be-tide thee, And bear thee thro' the e-vil days; Who trusts in God's un-chang-ing love Builds on the rock that naught can move.

2. What can these anx-ious cares a-vail thee, These nev-er-ceas-ing moans and sighs? What can it help, if thou be-wail thee O'er each dark mo-ment as it flies? Our cross and tri-als do but press The heav-ier for our bit-ter-ness.

3. Keep peace at heart, and wait His leis-ure In cheer-ful hope, and be con-tent To take what-e'er Thy Fa-ther's pleas-ure And all de-serv-ing love hath sent; Nor doubt our in-most wants are known To Him who choose us for His own.

4. Sing, pray, and keep His ways un-swerv-ing, So do thine own part faith-ful-ly, And trust His word; tho' un-de-serv-ing, Thou yet shalt find it true for thee; God nev-er yet for-sook at need The soul that trust-ed Him in-deed. A-MEN.

Alternative Tune, major (see opposite page)

57 I Leave All Things to God's Direction

Salom Franck, 1685
Tr. August Crull, 1923

WER NUR DEN LIEBEN GOTT LÄSST WALTEN (major melody)
9. 8. 9. 8. 8. 8. *Musikalisches Gesangbuch*, Hamburg

1. I leave all things to God's di - rec - tion, He lov - eth
2. My God hath all things in His keep - ing, He is the
3. The will of God shall be my pleas - ure While here on
4. God knows what must be done to save me, His love for

me in weal and woe; His will is good, true His af -
ev - er faith - ful Friend; He grants me laugh - ter af - ter
earth is mine a - bode; My will is wrong be - yond all
me will nev - er cease; Up - on His hands He did en -

fec - tion, With ten - der love His heart doth glow. My For - tress
weep - ing, And all His ways in bless - ings end. His love en -
meas - ure, It doth not will what pleas - eth God. The Chris - tian's
grave me With pur - est gold of lov - ing grace. His will su -

and my Rock is He: What pleas - eth God, that pleas - eth me.
dures e - ter - nal - ly; What pleas - eth God, that pleas - eth me.
mot - to e'er must be: What pleas - eth God, that pleas - eth me.
preme must ev - er be. What pleas - eth God, that pleas - eth me. A-MEN.

Alternative Tune, minor (see opposite page)

58 Whate'er My God Ordains Is Right

WAS GOTT TUT DAS IST WOHLGETAN

Samuel Rodigast, 1676
Tr. Catherine Winkworth, 1863   8. 7. 8. 7. 4. 4. 8. 8.

Weimar Gesangbuch, 1681
Severus Gastorius, fl. 1675

In well-defined rhythm

1. What-e'er my God or-dains is right; His ho-ly will a-bid-eth;
2. What-e'er my God or-dains is right; He nev-er will de-ceive me;
3. What-e'er my God or-dains is right; Here shall my stand be tak-en;

I will be still, what-e'er He doth, And fol-low where He guid-eth.
He leads me by the pro-per path; I know He will not leave me.
Though sor-row, need, or death be mine, Yet am I not for-sak-en;

He is my God; Though dark my road, He holds me that I
I take, con-tent, What He hath sent; His hand can turn my
My Fa-ther's care Is round me there; He holds me that I

shall not fall; Where-fore to Him I leave it all.
griefs a-way, And pa-tient-ly I wait His day.
shall not fall, And so to Him I leave it all. A-MEN.

59 Lord, as Thou Wilt, Deal Thou with Me

NUN FREUT EUCH

Kaspar Bienemann, 1574
Tr. Emanuel Cronenwett, 1880

8. 7. 8. 7. 8. 8. 7.

Melody by Martin Luther in
Geistliche Lieder, Wittenberg, 1535

1. Lord, as Thou wilt, deal Thou with me; No oth-er wish I cher-ish.
2. Grant hon-or, truth and pu-ri-ty, And love Thy word to pon-der;
3. When, at Thy sum-mons, I must leave This vale of sin and sad-ness,

In life and death I cling to Thee; Oh, do not let me per-ish!
From all false doc-trine keep me free. Be-stow, both here and yon-der,
Give me Thy grace, Lord, not to grieve, But to de-part with glad-ness.

Let not Thy grace from me de-part And grant an ev-er
What serves my ev-er-last-ing bliss; Pre-serve me from un-
To Thee my spir-it I com-mend; O Lord, grant me a

pa-tient heart To bear what Thou dost send me.
right-eous-ness Thro'-out my earth-ly jour-ney.
bless-ed end Thro' Je-sus Christ, my Sav-iour. A-MEN.

60 All Depends on Our Possessing

Alles ist an Gottes Segen
Author unknown, c. 1673
Tr. Catherine Winkworth, 1858, alt.　　8. 8. 7. 8. 8. 7.

ALLES IST AN GOTTES SEGEN
Johann B. König, 1738

Slowly and with dignity

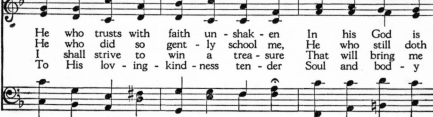

1. All de-pends on our pos-sess-ing God's a-bun-dant
2. He who hith-er-to hath fed me And to man-y
3. Man-y spend their lives in fret-ting O-ver tri-fles
4. When with sor-row I am strick-en, Hope my heart a-

grace and bless-ing, Tho' all earth-ly wealth de-part.
joys hath led me, Is and ev-er shall be mine.
and in get-ting Things that have no sol-id ground.
new will quick-en, All my long-ing shall be stilled.

He who trusts with faith un-shak-en In his God is
He who did so gent-ly school me, He who still doth
I shall strive to win a trea-sure That will bring me
To His lov-ing-kind-ness ten-der Soul and bod-y

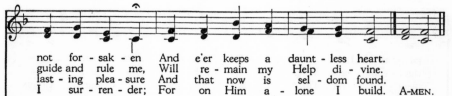

not for-sak-en And e'er keeps a daunt-less heart.
guide and rule me, Will re-main my Help di-vine.
last-ing plea-sure And that now is sel-dom found.
I sur-ren-der; For on Him a-lone I build. A-MEN.

61 God Is My Light

Ernst Wm. Hengstenberg, 1835. tr.   4. 6. 6. 4. 6. 6. 9. 9. 4.

GOTT IST GETREU
German Choral, 1850

Majestically

1. God is my Light! My soul, do not de - spair In hours of
2. God is my Trust! My soul, be not a - fraid, Thy Help - er
3. The King - dom His! Thro'-out the earth He reigns With wis - dom,
4. God is my Shield! Of me He takes the care As none be -

thy dis - tress! The sun with-draws, And earth is dark and drear:
will a - bide; "I'll not for - sake Thee!" He has kind - ly said,
grace, and might; The stars go on, And time its course main-tains
side could do; He guards my head, He watch - es ev - 'ry hair,

My light will nev - er cease. On days of joy with splen-dor beam - ing,
He's ev - er at Thy side; In fee - ble age will yet stand by thee,
Be - neath His watch-ful sight; In si - lence on-ward still pro - ceed - ing,
All dan-gers brings me through: While thou-sands, to vain help - ers call - ing,

Thro' nights of grief its rays are gleam - ing; God is my Light!
No re - al good will He de - ny thee: God is my Trust!
The u - ni - verse o - beys His lead - ing, The King - dom His!
On right and left are near me fall - ing, He is my Shield! A-MEN.

62   How Great the Joy to Be a Child of Jesus

Johann Jacob Rambach, 1693-1735
Tr. Moravian Coll.   11. 10. 11. 10. 8. 6. 6.   Chr. Gregor's Choralbuch, 1784

GREGOR

With confidence and joy

1. How great the joy to be a child of Je - sus, And to be guid - ed by His shep - herd staff; Earth's great - est hon - ors, how - so - e'er they please us, Com - pared to this are vain and emp - ty chaff; Yea, what this world can nev - er give,

2. Here is a pas - ture, rich and nev - er - fail - ing, Here liv - ing wa - ters in a - bun - dance flow; None can con - ceive the grace with them pre - vail - ing, Who Je - sus' shep - herd voice o - bey and know: He ban - ish - es all fear and strife,

3. Who - e'er would spend his days in last - ing pleas - ure, Must come to Christ and join His flock with speed; Here is a feast pre - pared, rich be - yond meas - ure, The world mean - while on emp - ty husks must feed: Those souls may share in ev - 'ry good

How Great the Joy to Be a Child of Jesus

May, through the Shep-herd's grace, Each need - y sheep re - ceive.
And leads them gen - tly on To ev - er - last -ing life.
Whose Shep-herd doth pos - sess The treas - ur -ies of God. A-MEN.

63   Lord, Thy Children Guide and Keep

DIX
Abridged from Chorale, *Treuer Heiland*

Bishop William W. How. 1854   7. 7. 7. 7 .7. 7.   Conrad Kocher. 1838

Joyously

1. Lord, Thy chil-dren guide and keep, As with fee - ble steps they press
2. There are sand - y wastes that lie Cold and sun-less, vast and drear,
3. There are soft and flow-'ry glades Decked with gold-en - fruit - ed trees;
4. Up - ward still to pu - rer heights, On - ward yet to scenes more blest,

On the path-way rough and steep Thro' this wea - ry wil - der - ness.
Where the fee - ble faint and die; Grant them grace to per - se - vere.
Sun - ny slopes and scent - ed shades; Keep them, Lord, from sloth - ful ease.
Calm - er re - gions, clear - er lights, Till we reach the prom - ised rest!

Ho - ly Je - sus, day by day, Lead us in the nar - row way. A-MEN.

64 Help Us, O Jesus, Thou Mighty Defender

Rev. R. A. John, 1912   11. 10. 11. 10. 11. 11.   REX MAXIMUS
Johann G. Hille, 1739

Reverently

1. Help us, O Je - sus, Thou might - y De - fen - der, Help when the
2. Help us, O Je - sus, in hours of temp - ta - tion, When both our
3. Help us, O Je - sus, when death shall spread ter - ror, And our poor

for - ces of e - vil ap - pear; Help us to bat - tle and
faith and our cour - age are weak; Teach us to look to the
eyes are too fee - ble to see; Cleanse us and purge us from

nev - er sur - ren - der, Help us to con - quer, and drive a - way
sign of sal - va - tion, And near Thy cross a new ar - mor to
sin and from er - ror, That we may blind - ly in faith cling to

fear; Sa - tan is cun - ning, the prince of de - ceiv - ers,
seek; Then we shall con - quer, if Thou wilt be - friend us,
Thee; Help us, O Je - sus, we con - quer in dy - ing,

Help Us, O Jesus, Thou Mighty Defender

Bring-ing dis - as - ter to man - y be - liev - ers.
Thou wilt pre - vail and our faith will de - fend us.
Un - to the last on Thy mer - cy re - ly - ing. A - MEN.

65 Draw Us to Thee

Zeuch uns nach dir
Friedrich Funcke, 1686
Tr. August Crull, †1923

ACH GOTT UND HERR
Andachts-Zymbeln
Freyberg, 1655

4. 4. 7. 4. 4. 7.

Slowly and with dignity

1. Draw us to Thee, For then shall we Walk in Thy
2. Draw us to Thee, Lord, lov - ing - ly; Let us de -
3. Draw us to Thee; Oh, grant that we May walk the
4. Draw us to Thee Un - ceas - ing - ly, In - to Thy

steps for - ev - er And hast - en on Where Thou art
part with glad - ness That we may be For - ev - er
road to heav - en! Di - rect our way Lest we should
King - dom take us; Let us for - e'er Thy glo - ry

gone To be with Thee, dear Sav - iour.
free From sor - row, grief and sad - ness.
stray And from Thy paths be driv - en.
share, Thy saints and joint heirs make us. A - MEN.

66 As the Hart with Eager Yearning

FREU' DICH SEHR (Comme un cerf)
Louis Bourgeois

Psalm xlii
Christine Curtis   8. 7. 8. 7. 7. 7. 8. 8.   Genevan Psalter, 1551

With flowing rhythm. May be sung in unison.

1. As the hart with ea - ger yearn - ing Seeks the cool - ing wa - ter-course,
2. Day and night in griev-ous an - guish Bit - ter tears have been my meat,

So my soul with ar - dor burn - ing Longs for God, its heaven-ly source;
While my long - ing soul doth lan - guish To par-take His man-na sweet:

When shall I be - hold His face? When shall I re - ceive His grace?
O, my soul, be not dis - mayed: Trust in God, who is our aid:

When shall I a - bide re - joic - ing In His presence, His praise voic - ing?
Hope and joy His love pro - vides thee; 'Tis His hand a - lone that guides thee. A-MEN.

Words used by permission of Miss Christine Curtis.

67 A Mighty Fortress Is Our God

Martin Luther. 1529
Tr. Frederick H. Hedge. 1853   8. 7. 8. 7. 6. 6. 6. 7.

EIN' FESTE BURG
Martin Luther, 1529

May be sung in unison. In majestic style.

1. A might-y fort-ress is our God, A bul-wark nev-er fail-ing;
2. Did we in our own strength con-fide, Our striv-ing would be los-ing;
3. And though this world, with dev-ils filled, Should threaten to un-do us;
4. That word a-bove all earth-ly powers, No thanks to them, a-bid-eth;

Our help-er He a-mid the flood Of mor-tal ills pre-vail-ing.
Were not the right man on our side, The man of God's own choos-ing.
We will not fear, for God hath willed His truth to tri-umph through us.
The Spir-it and the gifts are ours Thro' Him who with us sid-eth.

For still our an-cient foe Doth seek to work us woe; His craft and power are
Dost ask who that may be? Christ Je-sus, it is He, Lord Sab-a-oth His
The Prince of dark-ness grim, We trem-ble not for Him; His rage we can en-
Let goods and kin-dred go, This mor-tal life al-so; The bod-y they may

great; And, armed with cru-el hate, On earth is not his e-qual.
name, From age to age the same, And He must win the bat-tle.
dure, For lo! his doom is sure, One lit-tle word shall fell him.
kill; God's truth a-bid-eth still, His king-dom is for-ev-er.   A-MEN.

68 Who Puts His Trust In God Most High

Johann Mühlmann, 1573-1613
Tr. alt. Rev. C. G. Haas, 1898

8. 7. 8. 7. D.

PARIS
Arr. by J. Sebastian Bach, 1730

Majestically

1. Who puts his trust in God most just Hath built his house se - cure - ly;
2. Tho' fierc - est foes my course op-pose, A dauntless front I'll show them;
3. Thou art my kind con - sol - ing Friend, And Thou a - lone canst give me

He who re - lies on Je - sus Christ, Heav'n shall be his most sure - ly.
My cham-pion Thou, Lord Christ, art now, Who soon shall o - ver - throw them.
What-e'er I plead, in time of need; For this poor life I trust Thee.

Then fixed on Thee my trust shall be, Whose truth can nev - er al - ter;
And if but Thee I have in me With Thy good gifts and Spir - it,
Re - pent-ance true O grant a - new, And save me from all fol - ly;

While mine Thou art, not death's worst smart Shall make my cour-age fal - ter.
Nor death nor hell, I know full well, Shall hurt me, thro' Thy mer - it.
List to my cry, O Lord most High, My life make pure and ho - ly. A-MEN.

69 Rise, My Soul, to Watch and Pray

Mache dich, mein Geist, bereit
Johann B. Freystein, 1697; cento
Tr. Catherine Winkworth, 1863, alt.   **7. 6. 7. 6. 3. 3. 6. 6.**

STRAF MICH NICHT
Kirchen—und Hausbuch
Dresden, 1694

In moderate time

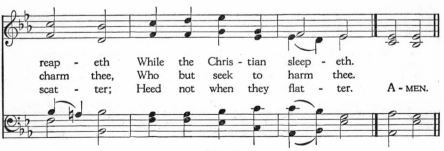

1. Rise, my soul, to watch and pray, From thy sleep a - wak - en;
Be not by the e - vil day Un - a - wares o'er - tak - en.
For the foe, Well we know, Oft his har - vest reap - eth While the Chris - tian sleep - eth.

2. Watch! Let not the wick - ed world With its pow'r de - feat thee.
Watch lest with her pomp un - furled She be - tray and cheat thee.
Watch and see Lest there be Faith - less friends to charm thee, Who but seek to harm thee.

3. Watch a - gainst thy - self, my soul, Lest with grace thou tri - fle;
Let not self thy tho'ts con - trol Nor God's mer - cy sti - fle.
Pride and sin Lurk with - in All thy hopes to scat - ter; Heed not when they flat - ter.

A - MEN.

70
In Thy Service Will I Ever

O DU LIEBE
Musikalischer Christenschatz

Carl Philip Spitta, 1836, tr.   8. 7. 8. 7. D.   Basel, 1745

Reverently

1. In Thy serv-ice will I ev-er, Je-sus, my Re-deem-er, stay;
2. Could I be in oth-er pla-ces Half so hap-py as with Thee,
3. Where shall I find such a Mas-ter, Who hath done my soul such good,
4. Let Thy light on me be shin-ing When the day is al-most gone,

Noth-ing me from Thee shall sev-er, Glad-ly would I go Thy way.
Who so man-y gifts and gra-ces Hast Thy-self pre-pared for me?
And re-trieved the great dis-as-ter Sin first caused by His own blood?
When the eve-ning is de-clin-ing, And the night is draw-ing on:

Life in me Thy life pro-du-ces And gives vig-or to my heart,
No one could be half so fit-ted To im-part true joy, I ween,
Is not He my right-ful own-er Who for me His own life gave?
Bless me, O my Sav-iour, lay-ing Thy hands on my wea-ry head;

As the vine doth liv-ing juic-es To the pur-ple grape im-part.
Since to Thee, O Lord, com-mit-ted Pow'r in heav'n and earth hath been.
Were it not a foul dis-hon-or Not to love Him to the grave?
"Here thy day is end-ed," say-ing, "Yon-der live the faith-ful dead." A-MEN.

71

Here Is My Heart

Ehrenfried Liebich, 1756, tr.   10 6. 10. 6. 8. 8. 4.   ICH HAB' GENUG
                    Johann Rudolph Ahle, 1662

Joyously

1. Here is my heart! My God, I give it Thee; I heard Thee
2. Here is my heart! In Christ its long-ings end, Near to His
3. Here is my heart! Ah, Ho-ly Spir-it, come, Its na-ture
4. Here is my heart! O Friend of friends be near, To make each

call and say, "Not to the world, My child, but un-to Me,"
cross it draws; It says, "Thou art my por-tion, O my Friend,
to re-new, And con-se-crate it whol-ly as Thy home,
tempt-er fly; And when at last I death a-wait with fear,

I heard and will o-bey. Here is love's of-f'ring to my King.
Thy blood my ran-som was!" And in the Sav-iour it has found
A tem-ple fair and true. Teach it to love and serve Thee more,
Give me the vic-to-ry! Then glad-ly on Thy love re-pos-ing,

Which, a glad sac-ri-fice, I bring, Here is my heart!
What bless-ed-ness and peace a-bound, My trust-ing heart!
To fear Thee, trust Thee, and a-dore, My cleans-ed heart!
Let me say, when my life is clos-ing, Here is my heart! A-MEN.

(65)

72 Father, Now Our Faith Confirm

H. Richard Niebuhr

Irregular

STÄRK UNS MITTLER
Composer unknown

With spirit

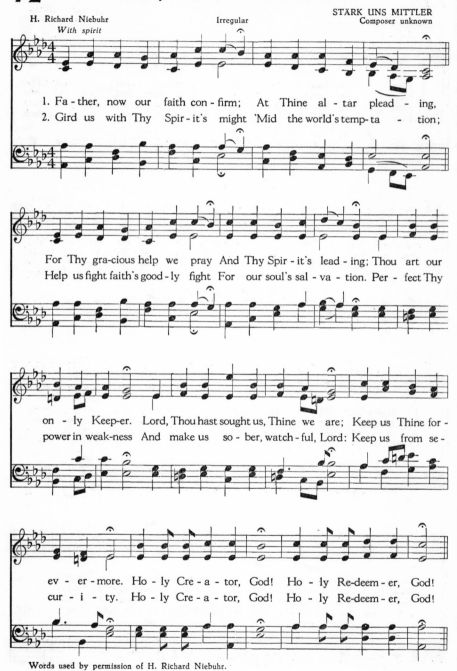

1. Fa-ther, now our faith con-firm; At Thine al-tar plead-ing,
2. Gird us with Thy Spir-it's might 'Mid the world's temp-ta-tion;

For Thy gra-cious help we pray And Thy Spir-it's lead-ing; Thou art our
Help us fight faith's good-ly fight For our soul's sal-va-tion. Per-fect Thy

on-ly Keep-er. Lord, Thou hast sought us, Thine we are; Keep us Thine for-
power in weak-ness And make us so-ber, watch-ful, Lord: Keep us from se-

ev-er-more. Ho-ly Cre-a-tor, God! Ho-ly Re-deem-er, God!
cur-i-ty. Ho-ly Cre-a-tor, God! Ho-ly Re-deem-er, God!

Words used by permission of H. Richard Niebuhr.

Father, Now Our Faith Confirm

Spir - it of God, Com-fort-er, Teach-er! Thou great Tri-une God! Make us
Spir - it of God, Com-fort-er, Teach-er! Thou great Tri-une God! Guide us

ev - er mind-ful Of our sa-cred pledge to Thee, Have mer-cy on us.
humble chil - dren In - to Thine a-bun-dant life, Have mer-cy on us. A-MEN.

73 My God, Accept My Heart This Day

NUN SICH DER TAG GEENDET HAT

Matthew Bridges, 1848   C. M.   Composer unknown

In moderate time

1. My God, ac - cept my heart this day, And make it al - ways Thine,
2. Be - fore the cross of Him who died, Be - hold I prostrate fall;
3. A - noint me with Thy heaven - ly grace, A - dopt me for Thine own,
4. Let ev - ery tho't and work and word, To Thee be ev - er given,

That I from Thee no more may stray, No more from Thee de - cline.
Let ev - ery sin be cru - ci - fied, Let Christ be all in all.
That I may see Thy glo - rious face, And wor-ship at Thy throne.
Then life shall be Thy serv - ice, Lord, And death the gate of heaven. A-MEN.

74   One Thing Needful, Greatest Blessing

Rev. R. A. John, 1916

8. 7. 8. 7. 12. 12. 11. 11.

EINS IST NOT
Joachim Neander, 1680

Slowly

1. One thing need-ful, great-est bless-ing, Teach me, Sav-iour, while I pray;
2. Oft my soul, in dark-ness grop-ing, Sought Thy peace in earth-ly scene;
3. Keep me, then, O Sav-iour, teach-ing Truth di-vine un-to my soul;

Fear and doubt, my heart op-press-ing, In Thy mer-cy drive a-way.
Blind-ly fear-ing, blind-ly hop-ing, Prone on earth-ly hope to lean.
That, be-yond the earth-born reach-ing, I may grasp the heav'n-ly goal.

Faster

The joys of this world, though in splen-dor they glit-ter,
But ev-er and ev-er in an-guish and sor-row
Re-plen-ish my soul from Thy heav-en-ly meas-ure

Will soon turn to ash-es, will soon be-come bit-ter;
I bur-ied the hopes of to-day and the mor-row;
And add to my earth-ly joys heav-en-ly pleas-ure,

The pleas-ure of pleas-ures that nev-er can die
For all that can bring me the soul's pure de-light
That ev-er my soul shall ex-ult-ing-ly sing

One Thing Needful, Greatest Blessing

From Thee on - ly com - eth, O Sav - iour on high.
Must come from a - bove, from the land of Thy light.
"Christ on - ly can save and Christ on - ly is King!" A-MEN.

75   Jesus, Still Lead On

Nicholas von Zinzendorf, 1721
Tr. Jane Borthwick, 1853

5. 5. 8. 8. 5. 5.

SEELENBRÄUTIGAM
Adam Drese. 1698

Moderately slow

1. Je - sus, still lead on, Till our rest be won, And, al -
2. If the way be drear, If the foe be near, Let no
3. When we seek re - lief From a long - felt grief; When temp -
4. Je - sus, still lead on, Till our rest be won; Heaven-ly

though the way be cheer - less, We will fol - low calm and fear - less;
faith - less fears o'er - take us, Let not faith and hope for - sake us,
ta - tions come al - lur - ing, Make us pa - tient and en - dur - ing;
Lead - er, still di - rect us, Still sup-port, con - trol, pro - tect us,

Guide us by Thy hand To our fa - ther - land.
For through man - y a woe To our home we go.
Show us that bright shore Where we weep no more.
Till we safe - ly stand In our fa - ther - land. A -MEN.

76 Jesus, Priceless Treasure

JESU, MEINE FREUDE
German Traditional Melody

J. Franck, 1618-1677
Tr. Catherine Winkworth, 1863

From J. Crüger's *Praxis Pietatis Melica*, 1656

6 6. 5. 6. 6. 5. 7. 8. 6.

Slowly and with dignity

1. Je - sus, price - less treas - ure, Source of pur - est pleas - ure,
2. In Thine arm I rest me; Foes who would mo - lest me
3. Hence, all thoughts of sad - ness! For the Lord of glad - ness,

Tru - est friend to me; Long my heart hath pant - ed, Till it well - nigh
Can - not reach me here. Though the earth be shak - ing, Ev - ery heart be
Je - sus, en - ters in: Those who love the Fa - ther, Tho' the storms may

faint - ed, Thirsting af - ter Thee. Thine I am, O spot - less Lamb,
quak - ing, God dis - pels our fear; Sin and hell in con - flict fell
gath - er, Still have peace with - in; Yea, what - e'er we here must bear,

I will suf - fer nought to hide Thee, Ask for nought be - side Thee.
With their heav - iest storms as - sail us: Je - sus will not fail us.
Still in Thee lies pur - est pleas - ure, Je - sus, price - less treas - ure! A-MEN.

77 Jesus, Thy Boundless Love to Me

Paul Gerhardt, 1653
Tr. John Wesley, 1739, alt.   8 .8. 8. 8. 8. 8.   VATER UNSER IM HIMMELREICH
Geistliche Lieder, Leipsic, 1539

With great dignity

1. Je - sus, Thy bound - less love to me No thought can
2. O grant that noth - ing in my soul May dwell but
3. O love, how gra - cious is Thy way! All fear be -

reach, no tongue de - clare; U - nite my thank - ful heart with Thee
Thy pure love a - lone; O may Thy love pos - sess me whole,
fore Thy pres - ence flies; Care, an - guish, sor - row melt a - way,

And reign with - out a ri - val there! To Thee a - lone, dear
My joy, my treas - ure and my crown! All cold - ness from my
Wher - e'er Thy heal - ing beams a - rise. O Je - sus, noth - ing

Lord I live, My - self to Thee, dear Lord I give.
heart re - move, May ev - ery act, word, thought, be love.
may I see, Noth - ing de - sire or seek but Thee! A - MEN.

(71)

78   In Thee Is Gladness

Johann Lindemann, 1631
Tr. Catherine Winkworth, 1863, alt.   Irregular

IN DIR IST FREUDE
G. G. du Corovoggis, 1591

1. In Thee is glad-ness A-mid all sad-ness, Je - sus, sun-shine of my heart; By Thee are giv - en The gifts of heav-en, Thou the true Re-deem-er art! Our souls Thou wak-est, Our bonds Thou break-est, Who trusts Thee sure-ly Hath built se-cure-ly, He stands for-ev - er: Hal-le-lu-ia! Our souls are pin-ing To see Thy shin-ing, Dy-ing or

2. His mer-cy bright-ens, Our work He light-ens, Songs of joy to Him we raise. All the earth sing-ing, With gran-deur ring-ing, Thank-ful hearts to Him in praise! Where-fore the sto - ry Tell of His glo-ry With heart and voi-ces; All heav'n re-joic-es In Him for-ev - er; Hal-le-lu-ia! We shout for glad-ness, Tri-umph o'er sad-ness, Love Thee and

In Thee Is Gladness

liv - ing To Thee are cleav - ing, Naught can us sev - er, Hal - le - lu - ia!
praise Thee, And still shall raise Thee Glad hymns for - ev - er: Hal - le - lu - ia!

79 Come, Follow Me, the Saviour Spake

Johann Scheffler, 1668
Tr. Charles W. Schaeffer, 1896

8. 7. 8. 7. 8. 8.

MACH'S MIT MIR, GOTT
J. Hermann Schein, 1628

In moderate time

1. Come, fol - low Me, the Sav - iour spake, All in My way a - bid - ing;
2. I am the Light, I light the way, A god - ly life dis - play - ing;
3. My heart a-bounds in low - li - ness, My soul with love is glow - ing,
4. Then let us fol - low Christ, our Lord, And take the cross ap - point - ed

De - ny your-selves, the world for - sake, O - bey My call and guid - ing. Oh,
I bid you walk as in the day, I keep your feet from stray - ing. I
And gra-cious words my lips ex - press, With meek-ness o - ver - flow - ing. My
And, firm - ly cling-ing to His Word, In suf-fering be un - daunt - ed. For

bear the cross, what-e'er be - tide, Take My ex - am - ple for your guide.
am the Way and well I show How you must so - journ here be - low.
heart, My mind, My strength, My all, To God I yield on Him I call.
who bears not the bat-tle's strain The crown of life shall not ob - tain. A-MEN.

80 From God Shall Naught Divide Me

Ludwig Helmbold, 1563
Tr. Catherine Winkworth, 1863

VON GOTT WILL ICH NICHT LASSEN
7. 6. 7. 6. 7. 7. 6.   *Christliche Tischgesänge*, Erfurt, 1572

Reverently

1. From God shall naught di - vide me, For He is true for aye
2. When man's help and af - fec - tion Shall un - a - vail - ing prove,
3. God shall be my re - li - ance In sor - row's dark - est night;

And on my path will guide me, Who else should of - ten stray.
God grants me His pro - tec - tion And shows His pow'r and love.
Its dread I bid de - fi - ance When He is at my right.

His right hand hold - eth me; For me He tru - ly car - eth,
He helps in ev - 'ry need, From sin and shame re - deems me,
I un - to Him com - mend My bod - y, soul and spir - it,

My bur - dens ev - er bear - eth Wher - ev - er I may be.
From chains and bonds re - claims me, Yea, e'en from death I'm freed.
They are His own by mer - it, All's well then at the end. A-MEN.

81 Thee Will I Love, My Strength, My Tower

Johann Scheffler, 1657
Tr. Catherine Winkworth, 1759   8. 8. 8. 8. 8. 8.   DU MEINER SEELEN
Arr. Henry Schwing

Joyfully

1. Thee will I love, my strength, my tower; Thee will I
2. I thank Thee, O e-ter-nal Sun, That Thy bright
3. Thee will I love, my joy, my crown; Thee will I

love, my joy, my crown; Thee will I love with all my power,
beams on me have shined; I thank Thee, who hast o-ver-thrown
love, my Lord, my God; Thee will I love, be-neath Thy frown

In all Thy works, and Thee a-lone; Thee will I love, till
My foes and healed my wound-ed mind; I thank Thee whose en-
Or smile, Thy scep-tre or Thy rod; What though my flesh and

sa-cred fire Fill my whole soul with pure de-sire.
liv-ening voice Bids my freed heart in Thee re-joice.
heart de-cay, Thee shall I love in end-less day. A-MEN.

82 My Life Is But a Pilgrimage

Friedrich Adolph Lampe, 1683-1729, tr.

8. 8. 9. 8. 8. 9. 8. 8.

WANDERER
Claude Goudimel, 1562

In moderate time

1. My life is but a pil-grim-age; A trav-'ler to my Fa-ther-land,
   I seek the Cit-y with foun-da - tion, Whose Builder, Mak-er is my God;
   And gain-ing there my blest a - bode, Would ev-er sing His great sal - va - tion.
   My life is here a pil-grim-age, I'm trav-'ling to my Fa-ther-land.

2. The hours of life's un-cer-tain day Haste on with-out a moment's stay,
   And, when once gone, are gone for-ev - er; They bear me to e - ter-ni-ty;
   Lord Je - sus, give me eyes to see, What e'er I need to know dis-cov - er!
   Nor let earth's vain de - lu-sions hide Thee from my sight, my on - ly Guide!

3. At times to me the Sun is bright, That Sun that sheds its gra-cious light,
   A - lone to bless the pure in spir - it: Then comes the roar-ing, rag-ing storm,
   So loud, ter - rif - ic its a - larm, So dark, I can-not help but fear it:
   But when I think of joys a - bove, My ter - ror yields its place to love.

4. Thou, Je - sus, once a pil-grim too, Wilt prove Thy-self a Help-er true,
   Of all my anx-ious cries, a Hear - er; Thy warn-ing word in mind I'll keep,
   And, by Thy guid-ance, ev - 'ry step Shall bring me to sal - va-tion near - er.
   My life and strength are wan-ing fast, Lord, with Thy con - so - la-tions haste! A-MEN.

83 Who Are These, Like Stars Appearing

Heinrich T. Schenk, 1719
Tr. Frances E. Cox, 1841-1864   8. 7. 8. 7. 7. 7.   EISENACH
                                                                 Joh. Christoph Bach, 1680

In moderate time

1. Who are these, like stars ap - pear - ing, These be - fore God's throne who stand?
2. Who are these of daz - zling bright-ness, These in God's own truth ar - rayed,
3. These are they who have con - tend - ed For their Sav - iour's hon - or long,
4. These are they whose hearts were riv - en, Sore with woe and an - guish tried;

Each a gold - en crown is wear - ing: Who are all this glo - rious band?
Clad in robes of pur - est white-ness, Robes whose lus - ter ne'er shall fade,
Wres-tling on till life was end - ed, Fol - lowing not the sin - ful throng;
Who in prayer full oft have striv - en With the God they glo - ri - fied:

"Hal - le - lu - jah!" hark, they sing, Prais - ing loud their heav'n-ly King.
Ne'er be touched by time's rude hand? Whence comes all this glo - rious band?
These, who well the fight sus-tained, Tri - umph thro' the Lamb have gained.
Now, their pain-ful con - flict o'er, God has bid them weep no more. A-MEN.

5 These like priests have watched and waited,
   Offering up to Christ their will;
Soul and body consecrated,
   Day and night they serve Him still:
Now in God's most holy place
Blest they stand before His face.

6 Lo, the Lamb Himself now feeds them
   On Mount Zion's pastures fair;
From His central throne He leads them
   By the living fountains there;
Lamb and Shepherd, Good Supreme,
Free He gives the cooling stream.

84 O City Fair, Jerusalem on High

Johann Matthäus Meyfart, 1626
Tr. Catherine Winkworth, 1858   4. 6. 6. 4. 6. 6. 7. 6. 7. 6.

JERUSALEM
Melchior Franck, d. 1639

With confidence and joy

1. O cit-y fair, Je-ru-sa-lem on high, Would God I were in thee!
2. O Zi-on, hail! Bright cit-y, now un-fold Thy gates of grace to me!
3. O what the tribe, Or what the glo-rious host, Comes sweeping swift-ly down?
4. In-num-'rous choirs Be-fore the shin-ing throne Their joy-ful an-thems raise,

My long-ing heart Fain, fain to thee would fly, It would not stay with me;
How man-y a time I longed for thee of old, Ere yet I was set free
The cho-sen ones On earth who wrought the most, The Church's bright-est crown
Till heav'n's glad halls Are ech-oing with the tone Of that great hymn of praise,

Far o-ver vale and moun-tain, Far o-ver field and plain,
From yon dark life of sad-ness, Yon world of shad-owy naught,
Our Lord hath sent to meet me, As in the far-off years
And all its host re-joi-ces, And all its bless-ed throng

It hastes to seek its foun-tain And quit this world of pain.
And God hath giv'n the glad-ness, The her-it-age I sought.
Their words oft came to greet me In yon-der land of tears.
U-nite their myr-iad voi-ces In one e-ter-nal song. A-MEN.

SUPPLEMENTAL HYMNS

85   Take Thou My Hand and Lead Me

Julie von Hausmann, 1867
Tr. R. A. John, 1912

7. 4. 7. 4. D.

SO NIMM DENN
Fr. Silcher, 1842

In moderate time

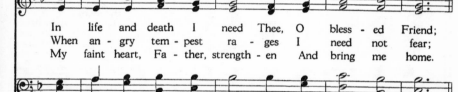

1. Take Thou my hand and lead me Un - to the end;
2. Thou might - y God of a - ges, O be Thou near;
3. When eve - 'ning's shad - ows length - en, The night is come,

In life and death I need Thee, O bless - ed Friend;
When an - gry tem - pest ra - ges I need not fear;
My faint heart, Fa - ther, strength - en And bring me home.

I can - not live with - out Thee For one brief day;
Close by Thy side a - bid - ing I fear no foe,
Take Thou my hand and lead me Un - to the end,

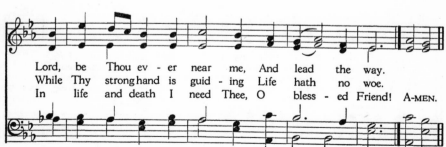

Lord, be Thou ev - er near me, And lead the way.
While Thy strong hand is guid - ing Life hath no woe.
In life and death I need Thee, O bless - ed Friend! A-MEN.

86   Wait on God, and Trust Him

Stanzas 1, 2 Friedrich Räder, 1845
Tr. J. H. Horstmann, 1908
Stanzas 3 and 4, J. C. Hansen, 1916   10. 11. 9. 11. 9. 10.

HARRE MEINE SEELE (Wait on God)
César Malan, 1827

1. Wait on God, and trust Him through all thy days; Cast thy cares up-on Him
2. Wait on God, and trust Him through all thy days; Cast thy cares up-on Him
3. Wait on God, and trust Him through all thy days; Cast thy cares up-on Him
4. Wait on God, and trust Him through all thy days; Cast thy cares up-on Him

who guides all thy ways. Do not de-spair; as the morn-ing fair
who guides all thy ways. Per - ish what will, God is ref - uge still;
who guides all thy ways. Take up thy cross; count it not a loss,
who guides all thy ways. On bend - ed knee, Lord, I cry] to Thee;

Scat - ters fog and dark - ness, God re-moves thy care. 'Midst all thy tri - als,
Great - er than the Help - er is not an - y ill. Faith - ful, e - ter - nal
For the heat of sor - row melts a - way the dross. Je - sus, dear Sav - iour,
Shield my soul from e - vil; to Thy cross I flee. Gra - cious Re-deem - er,

in all thy care God re-mains thy faith - ful Friend ev - ery - where.
Sav - iour and Friend, Save my soul from e - vil un - to the end.
pa - tient and mild, Let me be o - be-dient, a trust-ing child.
might-y and strong, Let me sing re - joic - ing the vic - tor's song. A-MEN.

87 Arise, Ye Soldiers of the Cross

Hieronymus Annoni, 1697-1770
Tr. J. H. Horstmann, 1919

8. 6. 8. 6. 6. 6. 8. 6.

TO ARMS
Anonymous

1. A - rise, ye sol - diers of the cross, To bat - tle for your Lord!
2. The sol - diers of this glo - rious King Re - ceive a rai - ment white,
3. Be strong, then, in your Lord and King, Put on God's ar - mor whole;
4. With Thee, our Cap - tain and our King, We need not fear the fight;

No sloth - ful soul can ev - er wield His strong, tri - um - phant sword.
And stand re - vealed to all the world As chil - dren of the light.
Be stead - fast in the e - vil day With true and right - eous soul.
If Thou dost rule each thought and deed, We con - quer by Thy might.

His ban - ner floats on high; Clear sounds the bat - tle - cry; With
They bear their Lead - er's cross, Care not for an - y loss, And
Take up the shield of faith, And, val - iant un - to death, Quench
Make strong each heart and bold, Nor let our love grow cold; Thy

Him who died to make us free We march to vic - to - ry!
ev - 'ry need is sat - is - fied As they in Him a - bide.
Sa - tan's ev - ery fier - y dart; Your Lord will strength im - part.
faith - ful sol - diers we would be And share Thy vic - to - ry. A-MEN.

88   I Now Have Found for Hope of Heaven

Johann Andreas Rothe, 1728
Tr. Henry Mills, 1850

MIR IST ERBARMUNG WIDERFAHREN
F. L. F. Hainlin, c. 1790
Alt. 1819

9. 8. 9. 8. 8. 8.

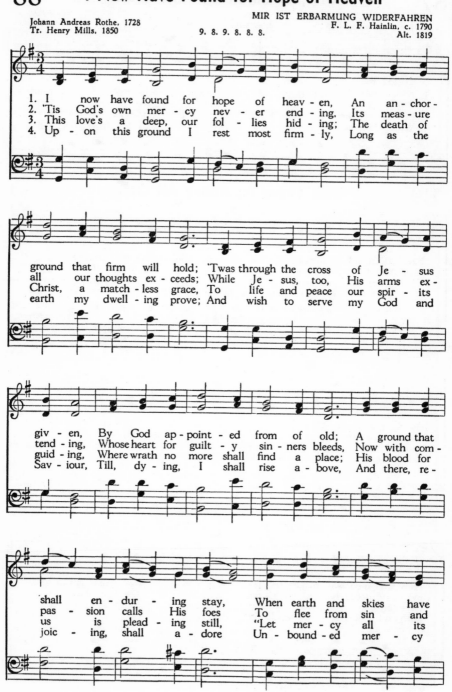

1. I now have found for hope of heav - en, An an - chor-ground that firm will hold; 'Twas through the cross of Je - sus giv - en, By God ap - point - ed from of old; A ground that shall en - dur - ing stay, When earth and skies have

2. 'Tis God's own mer - cy nev - er end - ing, Its meas - ure all our thoughts ex - ceeds; While Je - sus, too, His arms ex - tend - ing, Whose heart for guilt - y sin - ners bleeds, Now with com - pas - sion calls His foes To flee from sin and

3. This love's a deep, our fol - lies hid - ing; The death of Christ, a match - less grace, To life and peace our spir - its guid - ing, Where wrath no more shall find a place; His blood for us is plead - ing still, "Let mer - cy all its

4. Up - on this ground I rest most firm - ly, Long as the earth my dwell - ing prove; And wish to serve my God and Sav - iour, Till, dy - ing, I shall rise a - bove, And there, re - joic - ing, shall a - dore Un - bound - ed mer - cy

I Now Have Found for Hope of Heaven

passed a - way, When earth and skies have passed a - way.
end - less woes, To flee from sin and end - less woes.
work ful - fil, Let mer - cy all its work ful - fil!"
ev - er - more, Un - bound - ed mer - cy ev - er - more. A-MEN.

89 One There Is, Above All Others

Rev. John Newton, 1779   8. 7. 8. 7. 8. 7.   J. G. C. Störl. 1744

STÖRL

1. One there is, a - bove all oth - ers, Well de - serves the name of Friend;
2. Which of all our friends, to save us, Would con - sent to shed his blood?
3. When He lived on earth a - bas - ed, "Friend of sin - ners" was His name;
4. O for grace our hearts to soft - en! Teach us, Lord, at length to love;

His is love be - yond a broth - er's, Cost - ly, free, and knows no end;
But our Je - sus died to have us Rec - on - ciled in Him to God;
Now a - bove all glo - ry rais - ed He re - joi - ces in the same;
We, a - las, for - get too oft - en, What a Friend we have a - bove;

They who once His kind - ness prove, Find it ev - er - last - ing love.
This was bound-less love in - deed, Je - sus is a Friend in need!
Still He calls them "Brethren, friends," And to all their wants at - tends.
But when home our souls are brought, We will love Thee as we ought. A-MEN.

90 The Work Is Thine, O Christ Our Lord

Samuel Preiswerk, 1850
Tr. J. H. Horstmann, 1908

8. 6. 8. 6. 8. 8. 8. 8. 4. 6.

DIE SACH' IST DEIN
J. Michael Haydn, 1737-1806

In moderate time

1. The work is Thine, O Christ our Lord, The cause for which we stand;
2. Through suf-fering Thou, O Christ, didst go Un - to Thy throne a - bove,
3. Thou hast, O Sav-iour, led the way Through ag - o - ny and death;

And, be - ing Thine, will o - ver-come Its foes on ev - ery hand.
And lead-est now the self - same way Those true in faith and love;
O give, we pray, yet more and more Thy Spir - it's liv - ing breath!

Yet grains of wheat, be - fore they grow, Are bur - ied in the earth be-low;
So lead us, then, though sufferings wait, To share Thy kingdom's heavenly state,
Send mes-sen - gers o'er land and sea To bring Thy chil-dren all to Thee;

All that is old doth per - ish there To form a life both
Thy death hath bro - ken Sa - tan's might, And leads the faith - ful
Thy name can save, Thy name makes free; We con - se - crate our -

The Work Is Thine, O Christ Our Lord

new and fair: So too are we From self and sin made free.
to the light; E - ter - nal light, From dark - ness in - to light.
selves to Thee As serv - ants true, As war - riors brave and true. A-MEN.

91   Behold, How Good and Pleasant

F. G. Wetzel
Tr. by Rev. J. H. Horstmann   7. 6. 7. 6. 7. 6.

UNITY
Old Melody

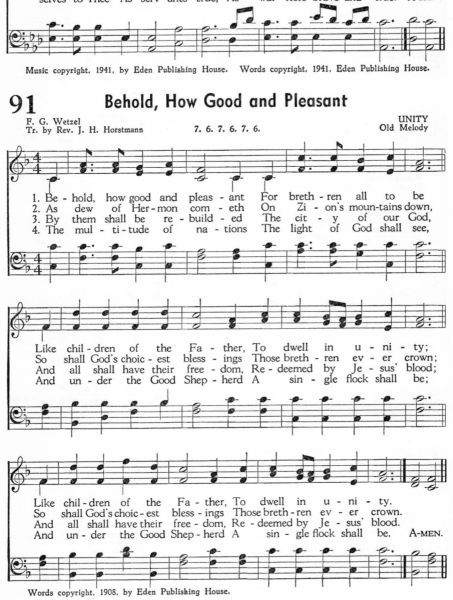

1. Be - hold, how good and pleas - ant For breth - ren all to be
2. As dew of Her - mon com - eth On Zi - on's moun - tains down,
3. By them shall be re - build - ed The cit - y of our God,
4. The mul - ti - tude of na - tions The light of God shall see,

Like chil - dren of the Fa - ther, To dwell in u - ni - ty;
So shall God's choic - est bless - ings Those breth - ren ev - er crown;
And all shall have their free - dom, Re - deemed by Je - sus' blood;
And un - der the Good Shep - herd A sin - gle flock shall be;

Like chil - dren of the Fa - ther, To dwell in u - ni - ty.
So shall God's choic - est bless - ings Those breth - ren ev - er crown.
And all shall have their free - dom, Re - deemed by Je - sus' blood.
And un - der the Good Shep - herd A sin - gle flock shall be. A-MEN.

92   I Know In Whom I Put My Trust

Ernst Moritz Arndt, 1819
Tr. in "Christ in Song"

C. M. D.

BETHLEHEM (Seraph)
Gottfried W. Fink, 1783-1846

1. I know in whom I put my trust, I know what stand-eth fast,
2. It is the Day-spring from on high, The ad - a - man-tine Rock,
3. Who once was borne, be-trayed and slain, At eve - ning to the grave;
4. There-fore I know in whom I trust, I know what stand-eth fast,

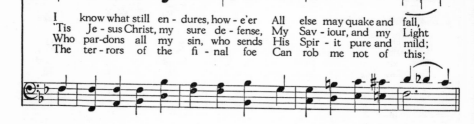

When all things here dis - solve like dust Or smoke be - fore the blast;
Whence nev - er storm can make me fly, That fears no earth-quake's shock;
Whom God a - woke, who rose a - gain, A Con - q'ror strong to save;
When all things formed of earth - ly dust Are whirl - ing in the blast:

I know what still en - dures, how - e'er All else may quake and fall,
'Tis Je - sus Christ, my sure de - fense, My Sav - iour, and my Light
Who par-dons all my sin, who sends His Spir - it pure and mild;
The ter - rors of the fi - nal foe Can rob me not of this;

When lies the pru-dent men en-snare, And dreams the wise en-thrall.
That shines with - in, and scat - ters thence Dark phan-toms of the night;
Whose grace my ev - 'ry step be-friends, Who ne'er for - gets His child.
And this shall crown me once, I know, With nev - er - fad-ing bliss. A-MEN.

93   I Sing the Praise of Love Unbounded

Gerhard Tersteegen
Tr. Rev. R. A. John, 1912

9. 8. 9 .8. 9. 9.

ST. PETERSBURG
Dimitri S. Bortniansky, 1825

1. I sing the praise of love un-bound-ed, Which God in Christ has shown to man; I sing of love that hath been found-ed Ere yet the stars their cours-es ran; The love that of-fers free sal-va-tion To sin-ful man of ev-'ry na-tion.

2. The love of God planned my sal-va-tion Be-fore I saw the light of day, And took a-way the law's dam-na-tion Of him, whose feet had gone a-stray; God's love is mine, O bless-ed mor-tal, And o-pens wide the heav'n-ly por-tal.

3. While life shall last, I'll sing the glo-ry Of Christ the Sav-iour and His love; With an-gel hosts I'll tell the sto-ry Of Christ in Zi-on's home a-bove; God's love is mine, death can-not sev-er Me from that heart that loves for-ev-er. A-MEN.

94 O Happy Home, Where Thou Art Loved the Dearest

Rev. Carl Spitta, 1833
Tr. Sarah B. Findlater, 1853

11. 10. 11. 10. D.

WIE WIRD UNS SEIN
German

1. O hap-py home, where Thou art loved the dear-est, Thou lov-ing Friend and Sav-iour of our race, And where a-mong the guests there nev-er com-eth One who can hold such high and hon-ored place! O hap-py home, where each one serves Thee low-ly, What-ev-er his ap-point-ed work may be, Till ev-'ry com-mon task seems

2. O hap-py home, where two in heart u-nit-ed In ho-ly faith and bless-ed hope are one, Whom death a lit-tle while a-lone di-vid-eth, And can-not end the un-ion here be-gun! O hap-py home, whose lit-tle ones are giv-en Ear-ly to Thee in hum-ble faith and prayer, To Thee, their Friend, who from the

3. O hap-py home, where Thou art not for-got-ten When joy is o-ver-flow-ing, full, and free; O hap-py home, where ev-'ry wound-ed spir-it Is bro't, Phy-si-cian, Com-fort-er, to Thee; Un-til at last, when earth's day's work is end-ed, All meet Thee in the bless-ed home a-bove, From whence Thou cam-est, where Thou

(88)

O Happy Home, Where Thou Art Loved the Dearest

great and ho - ly, When it is done, O Lord, as un - to Thee!
heights of heav - en Guides them, and guards with more than mother's care!
hast as - cend - ed, Thy ev - er - last - ing home of peace and love! A-MEN.

95   The Best of Friends I Have In Heaven

Tr. by Rev. J. H. Horstmann, 1908   9. 8. 9. 8. 8. 8.

THE DEAREST FRIEND
Louise Reichhardt

1. The best of friends I have in heav - en, The loy - al friends on earth are few;
2. The love of man is not a - bid - ing, While that of Je - sus nev - er wanes;
3. The world be - stows its greatest fa - vors On those who can and will re - pay;
4. He is the Friend a - bove all oth - ers, Whose heart and soul is whol - ly mine;

Where hearts to things of earth are giv - en, Friends can - not be sin - cere and true;
What - ev - er storms and ills be - tid - ing, This ev - er - faith - ful Friend re - mains:
When - ev - er for - tune's friend - ship wa - vers, Its fa - vors, too, will pass a - way;
Whose love is strong - er than a broth - er's, And stands beyond the end of time:

But firm - ly I can e'er de - pend On Je - sus as my dear - est Friend.
In joy and sor - row to the end My Sav - iour is my dear - est Friend.
With Je - sus such is not the end, He al - ways is the dear - est Friend.
Then praise with me un - til the end My Sav - iour as the dear - est Friend. A-MEN.

96   Striving Onward, Pressing Forward

Tr. Rev. J. H. Horstmann, 1908   8. 5. 8. 5. 7. 7. 8. 5.   STRIVING
Old Choral

1. Striv - ing on - ward, press - ing for - ward, Life di - vine to gain,
2. While con - tend - ing, and with - stand-ing For the truth and right;
3. In the sor - row which the mor - row May a - round us roll,

We will ev - er make en - deav-or Un - til we at - tain;
Draw us near - er, show us clear-er, Lord, Thy Spir - it's might;
Hold us ev - er, leave us nev - er, Save, O save the soul!

What de - tains we'll cast a - side, By that prom - ise to a - bide:
Let Thy word its strength im-part To each sad and yearn-ing heart;
Thro' temp - ta - tion's dai - ly strife, Thro' the van - i - ties of life,

Who en - dur - eth, life se - cur - eth, And the prize shall gain.
Praise a - bound-ing shall be sounding At Thy throne of light.
Lead us on - ward, for-ward, up - ward, To our glo-rious goal.   A-MEN.

97 Though Troubles Assail and Dangers Affright

John Newton, 1779

10. 10. 11. 11.

NICHT MENSCHLICHER RAT
German

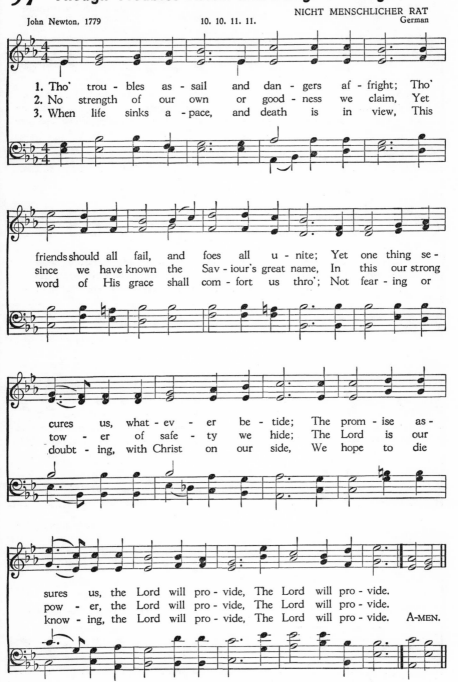

1. Tho' trou - bles as - sail and dan - gers af - fright; Tho' friends should all fail, and foes all u - nite; Yet one thing se - cures us, what - ev - er be - tide; The prom - ise as - sures us, the Lord will pro - vide, The Lord will pro - vide.

2. No strength of our own or good - ness we claim, Yet since we have known the Sav - iour's great name, In this our strong tow - er of safe - ty we hide; The Lord is our pow - er, the Lord will pro - vide, The Lord will pro - vide.

3. When life sinks a - pace, and death is in view, This word of His grace shall com - fort us thro'; Not fear - ing or doubt - ing, with Christ on our side, We hope to die know - ing, the Lord will pro - vide, The Lord will pro - vide. A-MEN.

98   We Plow the Fields, and Scatter

Matthias Claudius, 1782
Tr. Jane M. Campbell, 1861

7. 6. 7. 6. with Refrain

WIR PFLÜGEN (Dresden)
Johann A. P. Schultz, 1800

Brightly

1. We plow the fields, and scat-ter The good seed on the land, But it is
2. He on-ly is the Mak-er Of all things near and far; He paints the
3. We thank Thee, then, O Fa-ther, For all things bright and good, The seed-time

fed and wa-tered By God's al-might-y hand; He sends the snow in
way-side flow-er, He lights the eve-ning star; The winds and waves o-
and the har-vest, Our life, our health, our food; Ac-cept the gifts we

win-ter, The warmth to swell the grain, The breez-es and the sun-shine, And
bey Him, By Him the birds are fed; Much more to us, His chil-dren, He
of-fer For all Thy love im-parts, And what Thou most de-sir-est, Our

REFRAIN

soft re-fresh-ing rain.
gives our dai-ly bread.   All good gifts a-round us   Are sent from heaven a-
hum-ble, thank-ful hearts.

(92)

We Plow the Fields, and Scatter

bove; Then thank the Lord, O thank the Lord For all His love. A-MEN.

99 Be Thou Faithful Unto Death

Anon., tr. by Rev. J. H. Horstmann   7. 7. 8. 8. 7. 7.   FAITHFUL
Old Melody

1. Be thou faith-ful un-to death, Be thou faith-ful un-to death;
2. Be thou faith-ful un-to death, Be thou faith-ful un-to death;
3. To be faith-ful un-to death, To be faith-ful un-to death

Let not pain or sor-row ev-er From the cross of Christ thee sev-er;
Yon-der gleams the crown of glo-ry, And the an-gels tell the sto-ry,
I will con-stant-ly en-deav-or; Thou, O Sav-iour, help me ev-er,

Suf-f'ring till thy dy-ing breath, Faith-ful al-ways un-to death.
Echo-ing what the Spir-it saith: Be thou faith-ful un-to death.
While I draw this fleet-ing breath, To be faith-ful un-to death. A-MEN.

100 When the Weary, Seeking Rest

Horatius Bonar, 1867, alt. Irregular

RUHE IST DAS BESTE GUT
Johann Georg Stötzel, 1777

In moderate time

1. When the wea-ry, seek-ing rest, To Thy good-ness flee;
2. When the world-ling, sick at heart, Lifts His soul a-bove;
3. When the stran-ger asks a home, All his toils to end;
4. When the child with lov-ing heart, Youth or maid-en fair,

When the heav-y-la-den cast All their load on Thee;
When the prod-i-gal looks back To his Fa-ther's love;
When the hun-gry crav-eth food, And the poor a friend;
When the a-ged, trust-ing still, Seek Thy face in prayer;

When, crav-ing peace, Sin-ners on Thy name shall call,
When from their pride Proud men stoop to seek Thy face,
When in their pain Un-to Thee the sick do flee,
When, worn and sad, Fal-tering steps to Thee do turn,

At Thy feet re-pent-ant fall, Lord, hear their cry!
And the bur-dened ask for grace, Lord, hear their cry!
Lift to Thee their hum-ble plea, Lord, hear their cry!
Home-sick hearts for Thee do yearn, Lord, hear their cry! A-MEN.

101 Thy Word Is Like a Garden

EIN GAERTNER
Anonymous

Edwin Hodder. 1868

8. 6. 8. 6. 8. 6.

1. Thy Word is like a gar - den, Lord, With flow - ers bright and fair;
2. Thy Word is like a deep, deep mine; And jew - els rich and rare
3. Thy Word is like a star - ry host: A thou-sand rays of light
4. Thy Word is like an ar - m'ry grand Where sol - diers may re - pair
5. O may I love Thy pre - cious Word, May I ex - plore the mine,
6. O may I find my ar - mor there, Thy Word, my trust - y sword;

And ev - 'ry one who seeks may pluck A love - ly clus - ter there;
Are hid - den in its might - y depths For ev - 'ry search - er there;
Are seen to guide the trav - 'ler home And make his path - way bright;
And find for life's long bat - tle - day All need - ful wea - pons there;
May I its fra - grant flow - ers glean, May light up - on me shine!
I'll learn to fight with ev - 'ry foe The bat - tle of the Lord;

And ev - 'ry one who seeks may pluck A love - ly clus - ter there.
Are hid - den in its might - y depths For ev - 'ry search - er there.
Are seen to guide the trav - 'ler home And make his path - way bright.
And find for life's long bat - tle - day All need - ful wea - pons there.
May I its fra - grant flow - ers glean, May light up - on me shine!
I'll learn to fight with ev - 'ry foe The bat - tle of the Lord. A-MEN.

102 Ask Ye What Great Thing I Know

Rev. Benjamin H. Kennedy, 1863   7. 7. 7. 7. 7.   MEIN PREIS
German

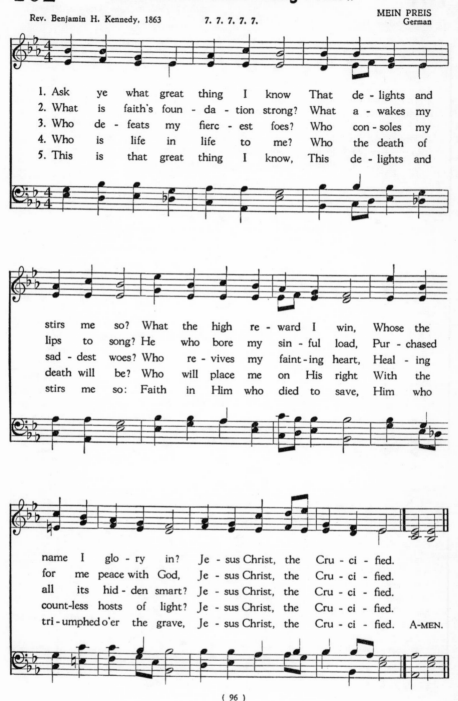

1. Ask ye what great thing I know That de-lights and
2. What is faith's foun-da-tion strong? What a-wakes my
3. Who de-feats my fierc-est foes? Who con-soles my
4. Who is life in life to me? Who the death of
5. This is that great thing I know, This de-lights and

stirs me so? What the high re-ward I win, Whose the
lips to song? He who bore my sin-ful load, Pur-chased
sad-dest woes? Who re-vives my faint-ing heart, Heal-ing
death will be? Who will place me on His right With the
stirs me so: Faith in Him who died to save, Him who

name I glo-ry in? Je-sus Christ, the Cru-ci-fied.
for me peace with God, Je-sus Christ, the Cru-ci-fied.
all its hid-den smart? Je-sus Christ, the Cru-ci-fied.
count-less hosts of light? Je-sus Christ, the Cru-ci-fied.
tri-umphed o'er the grave, Je-sus Christ, the Cru-ci-fied. A-MEN.

(96)

103 Fairest Lord Jesus

SCHÖNSTER HERR JESU (Crusader's Hymn)
Silesian Folk Song
German, 17th century   Irregular   Arranged by Richard S. Willis, 1850

In moderate time

1. Fair-est Lord Je-sus, Rul-er of all na-ture, O Thou of God and man the Son;
2. Fair are the mead-ows, Fair-er still the wood-lands, Robed in the bloom-ing garb of spring;
3. Fair is the sun-shine, Fair-er still the moon-light, And all the twink-ling, star-ry host;

Thee will I cher-ish, Thee will I hon-or, Thou, my soul's glory, joy, and crown.
Je-sus is fair-er, Je-sus is pur-er, Who makes the woeful heart to sing.
Je-sus shines bright-er, Je-sus shines pur-er Than all the an-gels heav'n can boast. A-MEN.

104 Thy Blessing, O Lord

G. L. Mosmann
Tr. J. H. Horstmann   6. 6. 10.   BENEDICTION
Old Melody

In moderate time

1. Thy bless-ing, O Lord, And peace us af-
2. Thy face ev-er bright With heav-en-ly
3. Thy coun-te-nance lift, And grant us Thy
4. That thus we may be For-ev-er with

ford; Pro-tect us and keep us from dan - ger.
light, Let shine now up-on us Thy chil-dren.
gift, The peace that a-bid-eth for-ev - er.
Thee: O Je-sus, say "A-men," yes, "A- men." A-MEN.

105 Evening and Morning, Sunset and Dawning

Paul Gerhardt, 1666
Tr. Richard Massie, 1857

5. 5. 5. 5. 10. 5. 6. 5. 6. 10.

DIE GÜLDNE SONNE
Johann G. Ebeling, 1666

With flowing rhythm

1. Eve - ning and morn - ing, Sun - set and dawn - ing, Wealth, peace, and
glad - ness, Com - fort in sad - ness, These are Thy works; all the
glo - ry be Thine! Times with - out num - ber, A - wake or in
slum - ber, Thou dost ob - serve us, From dan - ger pre - serve us,
Caus - ing Thy mer - cy up - on us to shine.

2. Fa - ther, O hear me; Par - don and spare me; Calm all my
ter - rors, Blot out my er - rors, That by Thine eyes they may
no more be scanned. Or - der my go - ings; Di - rect all my
do - ings; As it may please Thee, Re - tain or re - lease me;
All I com - mit to Thy Fa - ther - ly hand.

3. Griefs of God's send - ing Soon have an end - ing; Clouds may be
pour - ing, Wind and wave roar - ing, Sun - shine will come when the
tem - pest has past. Joys still in - creas - ing, And peace nev - er
ceas - ing, Foun - tains that dry not, And ros - es that die not,
Bloom - ing in E - den, a - wait me at last.

A - MEN.

(98)

106 From All That Dwells Below the Skies

From Psalm cxvii
Isaac Watts, 1719

8. 8. 4. 4. 8. 8. with Alleluias

LASST UNS ERFREUEN
Geistliche Kirchengesäng.
Cologne, 1623

In unison. Jubilantly

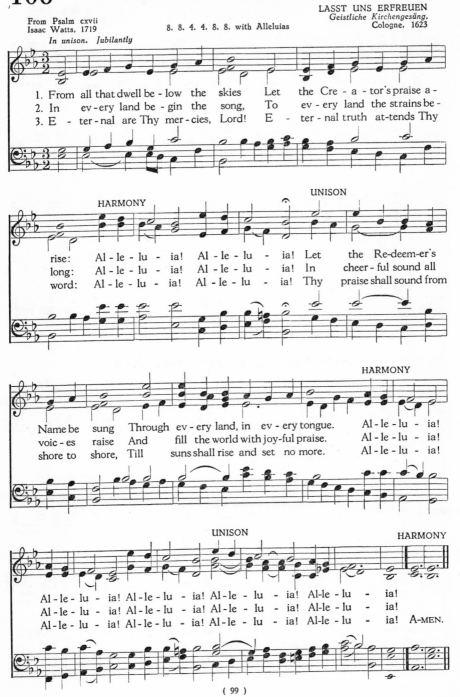

1. From all that dwell be-low the skies Let the Cre-a-tor's praise a-rise: Al-le-lu-ia! Al-le-lu-ia! Let the Re-deem-er's Name be sung Through ev-ery land, in ev-ery tongue. Al-le-lu-ia! Al-le-lu-ia! Al-le-lu-ia! Al-le-lu-ia! Al-le-lu-ia!

2. In ev-ery land be-gin the song, To ev-ery land the strains be-long: Al-le-lu-ia! Al-le-lu-ia! In cheer-ful sound all voic-es raise And fill the world with joy-ful praise. Al-le-lu-ia! Al-le-lu-ia! Al-le-lu-ia! Al-le-lu-ia! Al-le-lu-ia!

3. E-ter-nal are Thy mer-cies, Lord! E-ter-nal truth at-tends Thy word: Al-le-lu-ia! Al-le-lu-ia! Thy praise shall sound from shore to shore, Till suns shall rise and set no more. Al-le-lu-ia! Al-le-lu-ia! Al-le-lu-ia! Al-le-lu-ia! Al-le-lu-ia! A-MEN.

(99)

107

O Praise the Lord

Anon.

4. 7. 4. 7. 4. 4.

LOBT FROH
H. G. Nägeli, 1768-1836

1. O praise the Lord! He loves to hear you sing-ing; In sweet ac-cord
2. We bless Thee, Lord, While ev-'ry heart re-joi-ces, Thy name a-dored
3. Then ev-er-more In ev-'ry land and na-tion Tell o'er and o'er

Loud let your praise be ring-ing: O praise the Lord, O praise the Lord!
We sing with grate-ful voi-ces; We bless Thee, Lord, We bless Thee, Lord!
The ti-dings of sal-va-tion For-ev-er-more, For-ev-er-more. A-MEN.

108

Now the Light Has Gone Away

Frances R. Havergal, 1871

7. 7. 7. 7.

SILESIA
Silesian Air

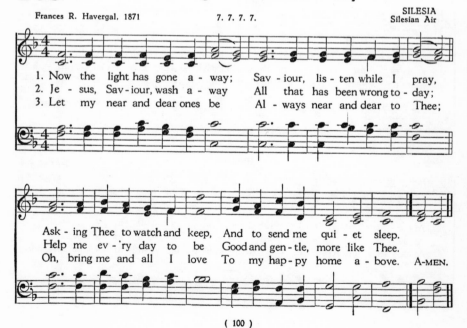

1. Now the light has gone a-way; Sav-iour, lis-ten while I pray,
2. Je-sus, Sav-iour, wash a-way All that has been wrong to-day;
3. Let my near and dear ones be Al-ways near and dear to Thee;

Ask-ing Thee to watch and keep, And to send me qui-et sleep.
Help me ev-'ry day to be Good and gen-tle, more like Thee.
Oh, bring me and all I love To my hap-py home a-bove. A-MEN.

Index of First Lines of Chorales

Index of First Lines of Chorales—*Continued*

Index of First Lines of Supplemental Hymns